SOMEONE WILL CONQUER THEM

By the same author

BE READY WITH BELLS AND DRUMS

SOMEONE
WILL
CONQUER
THEM

Elizabeth Kata

ST MARTIN'S PRESS
NEW YORK

'What though they conquer us?
The tea has come:
In at most nine hundred years,
Someone will conquer them . . .'
WITTER BYNNER

Part One

THE ATOMIC BOMB

1

Asama Yama lorded it over the village. He was a vulgar old mountain, suffering continuously from stomach disorders and a hole in the head.

Usually, a wisp of grey smoke drifted from his lacerated top-knot, but at times, rumbling and grumbling, he would give a thunderous roar, vomit crimson fire skyward, shower the surrounding countryside with fine ashes, and fill the people's nostrils with the harsh stink of sulphur.

When this happened at night-time, the foreign people who were living in the village that crouched at the volcano's foot leapt from their sleep-mats and beds in terror, thinking that they were at last the target of American bombing planes, those gigantic silver sharks so often seen swimming through the sky, on their ways to attack, mutilate and destroy other villages, towns and cities in Japan.

Before the war, the village near Asama Yama had been a summer resort for wealthy Japanese and for foreign residents of Japan; but, in 1944, it had become an eerie place, where the cream and dregs of many lands and nationalities huddled in overcrowded villas and serviceless hotels.

Diplomats and international adventurers, business men and their families, people from all walks of life, stood in the queues for meagre food rations. They were a polyglot crowd, distrustful of each other, awed by the despotic village police, and intimidated by war's most potent weapon – starvation.

They had fled from the terror of Japan's bombed cities, and many were refugees here who had been refugees before, to escape persecution and death in their home lands. Others, for varied reasons, had come to settle in, or visit Japan before the war.

Belonging to neutral countries, they were not interned, but left to fend for themselves. As the war years dragged by they felt that being interned would have simplified their lives.

The village had at first appeared to them as a safe haven, but just as the soft air of summer and the stark beauty of winter became a mockery, throwing misery into greater relief, so did the village become a prison. Once they were registered as residents there, a special pass to travel had to be obtained. War-torn, starving Japan had little time and thought for these foreign liabilities in her midst, during this, surely the most savage war in the history of mankind.

A rough track led from the village into the wooded hills. At a turn in the track a grey boulder protruded. From here, the entire village could be viewed. Further up, isolated in a hollow and surrounded by pinewoods, was a fragile Japanese house. This was the wartime refuge and home of Mary, the American wife of Goro Ogata, a Japanese.

A kindly man, her husband was twelve years older than Mary. During a stay in San Francisco, Goro had been offered the opportunity of working as assistant to her father, a brilliant biochemist. With interest and pleasure he had moved into the home of the American man, and it had embarrassed him when he saw that the daughter of the house was also the servant, overworked, unpaid and ill-treated.

He could not help noticing that some mornings Mary's hands were swollen, at times even bleeding, from beatings inflicted by her father. Her eyes were filled with shame, because of the sympathy that she saw in his eyes. As she served his morning meal he would talk to her, attempt to interest and amuse her. This was not difficult, and her fleeting smiles delighted him.

When he knew her better, he asked why her father treated her so cruelly. She told him that it was because of her mother's death. 'My mother died at my birth. My father loved her, and he hates me because I caused his tragedy.'

'Your father should have taken another wife,' Goro had said philosophically. 'It was his duty to give you a new mother. Sorrow should be aired in the open – never kept in the dark.'

He spoke of Japan, of the beauty, ancient customs and remarkable family unity in his homeland. When it was time for him to return there, and he saw the loneliness, the bereft expression on the girl's face, he had blurted out, almost without thought – which was unusual, for he was a thoughtful man – 'Come with me, marry me, Mary! Leave this life you are living. I promise you at least something better. . . .'

He had expected opposition from her father, and had again been shocked and puzzled when the older man had said, 'So you wish to marry my daughter – when?'

If Mary's father had not objected to his daughter marrying an Oriental, Goro's conventional Japanese parents had been infuriated and horrified by the marriage of their only son to a blue-eyed Occidental, and they had shown their dislike plainly.

A few months after Goro and Mary arrived in Japan, the Japanese attack on Pearl Harbor had occurred. Instead of the better life she had been promised, Mary was once more under parental disfavour.

Goro had taken her into his parents' household to live, in Japanese style. No one treated her cruelly – unless coldness and dislike is cruelty. She had learned to speak Japanese, but had no interest in learning their ways, especially after the order that Goro's mother, the mistress of the house, had given her, 'Please do nothing! I do not need your help!'

For more than a year, Goro, knowing that he had made a fatal mistake, did all in his power to make his American wife's life as pleasant as possible, under the difficult domestic and even more difficult wartime conditions. Eventually he had lost interest and openly agreed with his parents that he had done a foolish thing.

When the Ogata home was burnt to the ground during an air-raid, it was decided that this was the chance to rid themselves of the embarrassing enemy-American member of the family. They decided to send her to the foreign village near Asama Yama.

11

Goro had engaged as companion for Mary an English-speaking servant, Suzuki San, who had spent more than fifty of her seventy years working for British and American families in Tokyo. He had explained the situation to her; she understood perfectly and had no scruples against working for an American, war or no war.

Together, the old woman and the twenty-two-year-old girl had travelled to the mountain village, carrying with them a few personal possessions that had been salvaged from the fire. As the unbearably crowded train covered mile after mile, Suzuki was amazed and delighted to see the change that took place in her young mistress. 'She's pretty,' the old woman had at first decided, 'but, maa! she's a dull one.'

The trip, to Mary, seemed a journey to freedom. This, she felt sure, was the real beginning of her life. At least she was on her own, free of her father, her parents-in-law, and yes – Goro.

When they had eventually reached their destination, Suzuki's opinion was: 'She's pretty, and maa! she's a gay bright girl.'

2

On the afternoon of the very first day of their arrival, Mary said enthusiastically, 'Suzuki San, I'm going to the village. Can I shop, do something for you?'

'Shop? Do something? No shops open in village. Same here as in Tokyo – in all Japan, no shops, only hi-kyu – rations.'

'Oh! Well I'm going all the same.'

'O.K. I fix everything here. Poor little house, but I fix. Take care. I hear people in village most cold – not friendly.'

'To Japanese people, maybe, but not to me. Suzuki San, can you imagine how good it is for me to be among my own people again? I don't mean Americans, I mean . . .'

'You mean you very tired of Japanese.' Suzuki nodded her

head wisely. 'That's as life is. For such as you, Mary Sama, kimono-marriage is very bad.'

'Kimono-marriage? Oh! I see what you mean.'

'Certainly! Why not, my English is fine, so why not understand? I hear that in the village are many foreign women married to Japanese. I hear, most of them most glad, pleased with such marriage – having pretty, cute children. I hear that in the village are many people, Deutsch, Italia, France, people from everywhere. This village is like a pan of stew, not delicious stew, bad mixture. Nobody like nobody. Everybody not trusting nobody. I hear that in village Japanese police are watching, liking to catch, to punish. I hear that in village, many people are hungry and sick. I hear that in village . . .'

'Just a minute, Suzuki San, where did you hear all this?'

'In village.'

'But when?'

'This morning.'

'But you were there for less than an hour!'

Suzuki smiled proudly. 'So! For me an hour is enough to know everything there. Mary Sama, please take care in village.'

'Don't worry about me. I'll take care.'

Eager to find friends, Mary had walked down the hillside path gaily, expectantly, but none of the people she saw in the village noticed her; and the shops, as Suzuki San had warned her, were closed.

She wandered into the side lanes, past villas, their architecture sometimes pleasing, sometimes comical, but no one called to her in a friendly manner. The people she saw seemed worried, preoccupied with their own thoughts.

Despondently she returned to the main street, and there a down-at-heel man fell into step with her. 'Are you not German, lady?' he inquired, ingratiatingly. He spoke at first in German, then repeated the question in English.

'No, I'm an American,' she replied nervously.

'I am German.'

Whatever this man was, she did not like him, or his oily guttural voice.

'You have not been here, in the village, very long, lady, yes?'

'I arrived today.'

'Then perhaps you will like what I have to sell? I am right – yes?'

'To sell? I don't know – what do you sell?'

'Food, I sell food – price a little high maybe, but you would like some sugar, no?'

Sugar! So long since she had tasted anything sweet – more than a year. 'Sugar, yes, I would like to have some, and I don't mind how high the price.'

'You don't mind the price! I have other goods as well. Honey, cigarettes. Come to my room, I show you, you will come. Yes?'

The feeling that all this had happened before, and that it led to danger, was strong, but she stubbornly ignored the warning, and went on to the man's room that smelt of mouldering food, unwashed clothing.

From beneath an unpleasant-looking bed, a bag of sugar was produced. The price named was outrageous and she surely would never eat food stored amidst such filth.

'You have money on you, lady? I sell only for cash.'

'I have money.' Give him any price he asked, just get away quickly from this place, this repulsive man. 'I must go . . .'

'Not yet. Something else, perhaps? Cigarettes? Look, a length of English cloth – make a good, very good top-coat . . .'

'No, nothing else, just the sugar. I must go. . . .' Opening the rickety door, she walked into the arms of a Japanese policeman, who proudly escorted her along the darkening road, hustled her into the police station, imprisoned her there for buying food on the black-market. *Black-market!* That serious crime.

During the night, she heard Suzuki arguing with the policeman. Then, silence. In the morning the proud little policeman ordered excitedly, 'Captain Tanaka waits to see you.' He marched her to the main office and there was Captain Tanaka, Number One police officer of the village, looking at her, walking up to and around her, full of interest. He pointed to the bag of sugar that she still so foolishly held.

'Sugar, it is only sugar,' she stammered.

Captain Tanaka took the bag and emptied its contents on the floor. The heap of white crystals was a tiny replica of the snow-frosted volcano that towered over the village.

'You like sugar?' he smiled.

'Yes, yes, I do.'

'Then please eat it.' Still smiling he went to his desk, and became engrossed in his work.

Did he mean her to eat it now? All of it? He couldn't mean that. She began to scoop the crystals back into the bag.

'What are you doing?' asked Captain Tanaka, staring at her with unbelief.

'Do you mean that I must eat it all – now?'

'So! All! Now!'

'But . . .' she hesitated.

He stared unblinkingly, and apprehension thudded, like an unexploded bomb, in her heart.

For a timeless period they stared into each other's eyes. Eventually he squatted beside her, forcibly filled her hand with sugar, raised it to her mouth, his other hand on the soft nape of her neck.

She struggled; he was delighted; a shiver of – was it ecstasy? – ran through his body. Her teeth sank into his hand now pressed against her mouth – and she knew that he liked being bitten by her. Sugar gritted against her teeth, his blood mixed with it.

She was taken back to her cell, trembling and terrified.

For three days the battle continued. Captain Tanaka seemed to have little to do but sign papers and deal with her. On the fourth day, the round-faced policeman swept the now dirty sugar into a dustpan, and carried it away.

The fifth day, she stood to attention, her back against the wall in Tanaka's office. A stream of people came and went, bringing papers to be stamped. She gazed pleadingly at each newcomer,

15

but the men and women having their papers put in order had problems of their own. No one dared to get into the bad graces of the much feared police.

The final paper was stamped, Captain Tanaka cleared his throat, and spat into a neat piece of tissue paper, which he deposited fastidiously in the wicker trash basket. For a long time he stared silently at the wall before him, then, going to a covered table, whipped the cloth off it.

The table was set with knife, fork and spoon, snowy napkin, and yes – a plate of dirty grey sugar.

'I will never eat it,' she whispered, and it was then that she began to fathom the depth of the strange and unhealthy emotions she aroused in the man. His hands were restless, as though obsessed with desire to touch her. He looked ill, quite mad, and suddenly he placed a finger on the pulse that beat so wildly in her throat.

Footsteps sounded, the door opened, letting in a blast of cold wind – and Ludi Hoffer swaggered into the room.

His dark eyes expressed no amazement at the sight of a Japanese policeman holding a fair girl by the throat. Dumping his heavy rucksack down, he walked to the desk.

'Hah! Hoffer, you again?' Captain Tanaka spoke with furious bravado.

'That's right, me again,' Ludi said with a grin of self-confidence, and, as Tanaka attended to his papers, he winked wickedly at Mary. For no reason that she could comprehend, her hopes rose.

Tanaka ordered her to be taken back to her cell. Next day, he escorted her to the little house on the hilltop, where Suzuki San was waiting for her. 'You must not leave this house,' Tanaka ordered. 'If you go down to the village, you will be immediately arrested. I shall visit you here. I do not trust you.'

Daily, for more than a year, Mary had watched, through the torn paper window of her cottage prison, the comings and goings on the hillside track of Captain Tanaka; fearing and hating him with every nerve in her body.

3

LUDI HOFFER liked living in the mountain village; for it was both clean and beautiful. Shanghai, the city in which he had spent his past thirty years of life, was neither.

There were many things he liked about Japan; also some that puzzled, and yes – angered him. It was puzzling the way objects close by appeared so very far off. Asama Yama, for instance, looked close enough to touch; but, in reality, it was thirteen miles away.

His introduction to Japan had been a view from the sea of the glistening slopes of Fuji-Yama. It was said that within that mountain lived a 'Spirit Lady' who made the trees, shrubs and garden plants of Japan blossom.

Beautiful! But he admired Asama, even more.

The people of Japan were like the two mountains. Some possessed a dignity, an artistry, greatly to be admired. Was there, in the world, a finer example of human appreciation of nature, beauty, than in the proverbial poem of the humble water-carrier, who refused to break the spell of the morning glory blooming on the rope of his well, and went instead to beg water from a neighbour?

On the other hand, there were people in Japan who had no scruples about 'breaking' things – even people. It was difficult to believe they were of the same race.

Over the entire nation, like a pall, was the ingrained belief that fate was all-powerful. Shigatakanai! It can't be helped! One heard it repeatedly. Ludi ignored this, for he knew that most things could be given a shove, changed quite a bit.

Having no country of his own, he couldn't understand the sacrificial, and, to his way of thinking, ignorant Japanese patriotism. It seemed foolish to him – as foolish as it was wonderful to the Japanese – to see a young pilot jump to his death from a burning plane, over his own country, from an aircraft that possibly could make a safe landing. He had seen that happen right over Tokyo city. Japanese onlookers had wept proudly, applauded, but it angered and upset Ludi. He didn't like not understanding things, and he didn't like waste.

He admired the industry of the people, envied the unity of their family life. Some of these paradoxical people admired his fluency in speaking their language; others were quite annoyed, preferring to think their language was not easy to pick up.

Peacetime Japan, he knew, had been a land of airy uncluttered houses, happy, cared-for, children. Silken kimonos, stiff brocaded obi-sash; countless lovely things. Someone had once said: 'If you want heaven on earth, get yourself a Japanese wife, a Chinese cook, and live in an American house.'

True for some men, perhaps, but he had lived in the Orient all his life. When he married, he'd like a wife fair and blue-eyed. The thought brought Mary Ogata to mind. He had heard it said in the village that Captain Tanaka was bewitched by the American girl living in the small mountain-top house.

Ludi often went to Mary's house, but *he* wasn't bewitched. At times she irritated him with her stubbornness, her up-in-the-air opinions, her helplessness. If she weren't so helpless, and, yes, beautiful, he would not have been bothered seeing that she had enough to eat, to smoke.

He wished that he could rid her of Tanaka's persecution. How terrified she'd been that day when he had first seen her at grips with the Japanese policeman. It had been an ugly sight. His nature couldn't ignore the under-dog, couldn't endure dictatorship. True, he'd gone out without doing anything, but he knew the Japanese. He had put a trick phone call through to Tanaka, sent him scuttling down the street as though on his way to capture President Roosevelt. The false information had kept the policemen busy for several days. It had been amusing; and amusing, too, thinking back, the way he himself had gone to the police station, and had bought the dirty pile of sugar, bought it at black-market price from the two inoffensive little policemen whose faces had brightened considerably at his entry. That was natural, for without him they wouldn't have extra tobacco and at times even a bottle of illicit rice-wine. He'd given them plenty, to keep their mouths shut about his dark business deals.

He was making another fortune up here, in the seemingly starvation-ridden Alpine district. People were willing to pay any price for food these days, but had no initiative to get things for themselves, and they were scared stiff of the police.

He didn't really like what he was doing, but couldn't sit around, doing nothing, waiting for the war to finish. The Japanese attack on Pearl Harbor had been a knife in his back, too. He had just previously escaped from Shanghai, brought his illegally gotten dollar-yen exchange wealth with him, planning to get as quickly as possible to the United States: but how unlucky could a man be? Here he was, a rich man at last, stuck in Japan for the duration of the war.

When bombing had become heavy in Tokyo, this village, discovered, it was said, by Christian missionaries as an escape from coastal humidity, had seemed the very place to go to. It was also said that the Americans knew that the valley was crowded with non-Japanese people, and that they would never bomb, never destroy it. So far, so good! Things could be much worse. It was strange the way that Tanaka was letting him get away with his flagrant black-market dealings. Quite a few men from the village were languishing in prison for doing much less.

And tomorrow would be Christmas Day! Before tomorrow came he'd pick up that load of sugared persimmons from the Usami farm, and hand them out to children he knew. Children, Christmas and war – what a combination!

Square-shouldered, olive-skinned, a slightly off-beat nose on his handsome face, Ludi wore a tough expression that disappeared only when he smiled.

He smiled now, for there was Suzuki San trotting down the road towards him. He liked her; she was a grand old woman.

Today, one of the policemen who had sold that sugar to him was leaving for the war. Poor cuss! Dressed in an ill-fitting uniform, such a miserable look on his young face. The relatives and friends farewelling him were a hangdog lot too. What were they yelling? Of course – Banzai. What did it mean, exactly? Victory – a sort of three cheers. . . .

How would it be if every nation in the world had one burning desire – a desire for peace – and shouted out together a sort of international banzai? How would that be?

4

MARY lay on the thin floor-mattress, wishing that morning had not come. Pulling the worn blanket over her head, she made a fragile pool of warmth, breathing out deeply and slowly. The air in the room was so cold it had hurt her throat.

In the garden, Suzuki was battling with blunt axe and stubborn, damp, pine logs. She never swore in her own language; but she blasphemed, and slang-talked, with ease and gusto in English.

Her words gathered momentum, and Mary, winding the blanket about her body, went to the paper window. 'No. Suzuki San – no, no! It's Christmas Day! You can't talk like that on Christmas Day!'

'I can,' came the strong answer.

'Please!' begged Mary.

Suzuki, chin resting on the handle of her axe, looked at the face peering through a gaping hole in the rice-paper. The face was too thin, but she liked it very much. 'O.K.' she grunted.

Since childhood, Mary's Christmas Days had been gloomy and disappointing, but never one as drear as this. As the day wore on, she became so depressed that Suzuki took her to task.

'Life will grow better, Mary Sama, good time will come, see if it don't! These bado times will help make you kerei, beautiful.'

'Beautiful? Why, I'm getting lines on my face . . .'

'Hah!' interrupted Suzuki firmly. 'Lines on young face show person has lived. If same face can smile, shows person has lived with courage.'

'Courage!' scoffed Mary. 'A lot of good courage has done me. I consider that I show great courage when Tanaka uses my hands to stub out his cigarettes, instead of an ashtray. I'm in agony with my hands, there's scarcely a place left to burn. Suzuki San; have we any salve left for them?'

As she gently applied salve to the swollen livid hands, the old servant spoke tersely. 'Such a man, that Tanaka – he can't be Japanese – no Japanese could be so bad like him.'

'Is that so?' Mary cried indignantly. 'To me, it seems that Captain Tanaka is the very spirit of Japan, cruel, humourless . . .'

'No, no, not as you say, Mary Sama! I am Japanese, never hurt nobody. Many Japanese people the same as me.'

The old woman was so distressed that Mary smiled, and said gently: 'Take no notice of what I say, Suzuki San! I mean only part of what I say these days.'

'Now that's a poor thing to do. Person should say all of what mean – not just part. Mary Sama – that is your habit, it is bad, you must mend your habit.'

Mary looked sulky. 'How can I help it? Each year of my life, as the years pass by, is more lonely and senseless than the last. When I think back on my miserable childhood: no mother, my father cruel to me, my foolish marriage . . .'

'Hah! Enough of such back-looking talk,' cried Suzuki. 'Saa! Now today is God's birthday, isn't it?'

'Christ's birthday,' mumbled Mary.

'Same thing! Anyone's birthday is reason to make cheerio. So let us make a Christmas tree.'

'What with?'

'With tree of course. If we have something not poor of, it is trees.'

'Nothing to decorate it with.'

'I make little paper storks.'

'We have no nice paper.'

'We have Chiri-gami, very nice, very white, will make lovely happy storks.'

'Toilet paper! But – ah, Suzuki San, you slay me, I love you.'

'You get red string and wind around acorns,' Suzuki grinned proudly.

'Ah – huh! And we have silver paper from Ludi's cigarettes. . . .'

Christian and Buddhist sat that evening on the cold floor, adoring the peculiar, appealing little tree. The green tea, the bitter gluey bread, became a feast of celebration.

'Now, perhaps a game of rummy?' delicately suggested Suzuki. She was a card expert, and Mary had acted quite pettishly after their last game, on discovering that the few games she had won were with the compliments of her smarter opponent.

'Yes, let's play!' Mary shuffled the torn cards gingerly.

As they settled down to their game, footsteps came trudging up the rough frozen track.

'It's him – Tanaka!' whispered Mary.

'It's him – Ludi San,' stated Suzuki firmly.

Glowing with health, Ludi brought into the room, as well as his heavy rucksack, the feeling of life. Suzuki became an officious hostess and Mary wished that she had put on at least a little lipstick.

'Ho! A gambling den!' exclaimed Ludi. 'Don't you girls know that gambling in wartime Japan is against the law? I'm surprised. Here's your Christmas present, old lady.' He tossed a parcel to Suzuki, who cooed when she opened it and saw a small, velvet-covered metal box. 'An okairo, a little body stove!' Firing a charcoal stick, and putting it into the box, she tucked it down her obi-sash. 'I shall be warm now. Domo arigato, domo arigato! Thank you, thank you!'

She took the black-market food from Ludi's rucksack, and hid it in the tiny attic, where even her height of four feet eleven inches was higher than the wooden ceiling.

Ludi poured some of the rice wine he had brought into two tea-bowls.

'I wish that I had some cups with handles,' said Mary. 'I hate these bowls – everything Japanese.'

'I like these cups, and I like many things Japanese.' Settling back with a sigh of contentment, he continued, 'I'd a hard time getting here tonight. The police stopped me, and inquired into the contents of my rucksack.'

'Oh, God! What happened?'

'I left them, their pockets bulging with cigarettes,' laughed Ludi. 'Just as I left, Tanaka sneaked into the station and glared at me.'

'Oh, God! Did he?'

'Mary, just because this happens to be Christmas Day, do you have to begin every sentence with your Creator's name? It's very monotonous, and you're dull company, lady.'

'Did I, am I? Oh, Ludi, what a dreadful Christmas Day it's been!'

'I like Christmas, always have. Went to church this morning.'

'Church?'

'Yes, no one said we couldn't have church, so we had it.'

'Heavens!'

'There you go again. I had no idea you were of such a saintly turn of mind.' He gazed at her in psuedo admiration and once again filled the cups with sakē. 'As I was saying, I've had a fine Christmas Day. The kids in the village were happy; scrawny, cold, but happy. I was able to get hold of some sugared persimmons for them. I like children.'

'Humph!' Mary emptied her cup. She was feeling warm for the first time in months. 'I never knew any children, not really, and I notice you didn't bring a gift for me – and Ludi, the prices you charge me for food and cigarettes are disgraceful.'

'I give presents to old women and children, never to young women. If my price is too high for you, lady, you don't have to buy. I'm not like the old pedlar in the classic poem who cried up his wares with the argument that, because he was a poor man, everybody who could afford to do so should buy from him. That's not my line of sales-talk. I say, buy if you want to. If

23

you don't, be cussed to you. I'm coming out of this war a rich man.'

'Suzuki San says that you will die young if you are not more careful.'

'I have great respect for Suzuki San's opinion, but, in this case, she also can be cussed.'

'That's a silly word you keep using.' Mary gave a tiny hiccough. 'Pour me more of the sakē, please.'

'Suzuki San is wrong,' continued Ludi. 'And, to change the subject, you look more forlorn than ever. Has Tanaka been here today?'

'No.'

'Why've you been crying, then?'

'I have not been crying.'

'You have been crying; certainly you have been crying. I always know when a girl has been crying.'

'You know! You always know so much,' muttered Mary.

'That's right. I can also tell you why you've been crying.' Lighting a cigarette, he inhaled deeply. 'You cried because you are convinced that you have troubles, but you don't know what real trouble is. *You* suffer from a lack of guts. "I've never lived," you cry. What are you doing right now? Living, aren't you?' He stubbed out his cigarette impatiently.

Suzuki came and thriftily shook the precious tobacco into a tin, to roll again and smoke in the fine paper of her English-Japanese dictionary.

He smiled at the old woman and carried on with his lecture. 'Don't sulk, Mary! You're a good-looking girl, your face is a honey-coloured triangle, eyelashes a gift from heaven, and your figure reminds me of Mei Ling.'

'Who is she?'

'A Chinese lady of very easy virtue and quite a dish.' He half closed his eyes, sighing reminiscently.

'Really, Ludi!'

'There, you see! Pretending to be shocked. Why don't you ask me to tell you more about her? All virtuous women adore hearing details about their unvirtuous sisters. You are virtuous?'

'You are disgusting.' She laughed, reluctantly.

'You, as usual, have led me off the main track. Oh, yes! You don't know what trouble is. Now, Chang is a friend of mine in Shanghai . . .'

'You and your friends!'

'Chang was born without any arms or legs, born of a beggar mother; that could be trouble – but Chang! He rolls himself along the street yelling curses, making people give him right of way, finds a spot he likes, plants his old bottom on a cushion, leans his hump back against a wall, and begins the day's work.'

'What could he do? No arms, no legs?'

'He's a crack shot, runs a gambling school. Double or nothing that he's a better shot than the other fellows.'

'He couldn't! No arms or legs!'

'Ah, you see! But Chang has guts. He shoots with the spit of his mouth, the competitor names the target and *fffer whit!* I never saw him miss. He runs a thriving business.'

'I don't believe you,' stated Mary flatly.

'Who cares what you believe? Who cares for the opinion of a girl who has never lived? Your marriage is a flop, but you did the marrying. You're cold and practically starving – you, and millions of other people. A stinking policeman comes to your house and threatens you, burns your little hands with his cigarettes, and you think you're Jeanne d'Arc.'

'I don't, I don't!'

'Oh, you do, you do,' teased Ludi. 'Mary, I must go. If I don't, I'll miss my Christmas present.'

'Christmas present?'

'Mei Ling is not your only sister of easy virtue. Even here, in the village . . .' With a hearty laugh, he shrugged into his leather coat.

'Do you have to go, Ludi?'

'I do, unless of course – you . . .?' He grinned wickedly.

'I have not drunk *that* much sakē.'

'So!' His grin vanished, he looked at her thoughtfully. How pretty she was and for all her fragility she could throw a punch; surprising, too, how it found its mark. 'Why! You do have some guts, Mrs Ogata!'

'I? Surely not, I know you think me . . .'

'What?'

She hesitated. 'Well, wishy-washy. Do you know what that means?'

'I know.'

'Well?'

'Well, what?'

'Well, do you think of me like that?'

'Yes.'

'Oh! Then, is that why you have never tried, never . . .'

'Go on.'

'I think perhaps I have drunk too much sakē.'

'Maybe you have,' agreed Ludi uninterestedly. 'Gooda nighto! As Suzuki San would say.'

He slid open the door. Snow was falling and a blast of cold air filled the little house. Mary shivered. Before the closing door hid him completely from sight she called, 'Ludi!'

'What the hell do you want now?'

'Nothing, nothing really – you can go.'

'Mary, I had "gone," but you called me back.' He waited impatiently.

'I was going to ask you if your opinion of me is the reason you've never . . . I'm glad that you haven't. But, I just wanted to know why you've never . . .'

The grin was back on his face. 'I never saw you more charming, your face is on fire.'

She put her hands to her cheeks. Burning indeed! Why had she started this? She should have known, remembered, that she always came off second best.

'So, Mary, you want to know why I haven't taken advantage of your lonely plight on the mountain-top? You wonder why I have been able to resist your charms?'

'You are always so vulgar.'

'And you! So unsubtle. Why don't you say, "Why haven't you at least attempted to make love to me, Ludi Hoffer?" That's what you mean, isn't it?'

'Something like that,' she whispered.

He laughed. 'I didn't know there was anything like that. Let me into your secret, I'm always eager to learn. No? Of course not! *That* would be living. Mary, making love to you would be like taking candy from a baby, a very young baby and asleep at that.'

The door slid open, then shut. He was gone and she crept into bed, fully clothed.

5

THE year 1945 began. In the village, starvation point had come, and the people longed for spring to arrive, for then the cold would be one discomfort less to endure. Surly young Japanese soldiers were now stationed throughout the village, bright sharp bayonets fixed to their rifles. This supervision drew the people more closely together, and some, of different nationalities, who had not spoken to one another since the war began, now asked each other, 'What is going to become of us?'

Ration markets were now mostly closed, and people who had not been able to hoard a secret supply of food were filled with the deepest dread.

Captain Tanaka had ordered Ludi Hoffer to keep away from the house of Mary Ogata, and Tanaka was now her only caller.

One day, with astonishment, Mary saw Goro Ogata walking up the track towards the house. What had brought him? How thin, how exhausted he appeared.

'I've been worrying about you, Mary. I came to bring you money.'

'There's not much that I can do with money here.'

'I suppose not. Mary, my parents are dead. They were travelling by train, escaping to the country – away from the bombings. . . .'

'I am sorry.'

'Are you?' he asked sceptically.

'I said I am sorry. They were your parents, you were fond of them.'

'Fond! I loved them.' He buried his head in his hands.

She watched him uneasily, unable to speak a comforting word, and feeling ashamed because this was so.

Going to the window, he fingered the torn paper. 'Why don't you mend this window?'

'What?'

'The paper, the window. It looks so untidy, I should think two women, you or the old woman, could fix this.'

'Who cares about the window?'

'I couldn't stand it,' he answered simply.

'Tell me more about Tokyo?'

'Things are shocking,' he began. 'The city is going up in flames; raids are continuous, people are starving, terrified, dirty.'

'How much longer will it be before the end? It must end. Soon, it *must* – it *has* to. What is going to happen then?' asked Mary.

Straightening his shoulders, deepening his voice, Goro said solemnly, 'We Japanese will never allow American troops on our shores. We shall never surrender.'

'Never? That's a big word.'

'Small children are sharpening sticks with which to fight the enemy.'

'Must you talk like a child?' Mary spoke impatiently.

'It is true.'

'Then, you do expect to be defeated?'

He sat beside her. 'Not only expect, Mary – know.'

'What will you do?'

'Do? Like any true Japanese, I should kill myself.'

She looked at him curiously. 'How?' she asked, and imme-

28

diately regretted her question, for the expression on his sensitive kindly face was one of shame, for her. 'You surely wouldn't be so foolish,' she said gently.

A few hours later, watching him walk down the track, she knew only relief, and once again was ashamed, for from him she had received, always, nothing but kindness. She had been tempted to tell him of her trouble with Tanaka – but what could he have done about it? Exactly *nothing* – she felt relieved not to have burdened him with her problem.

6

MARY and Suzuki spent much time discussing the fact that Ludi Hoffer no longer called to see them. They knew that he was still at large and in the village, and that at times, in the dark of night, he came up the track, for they would find parcels of food left at their door.

'Why don't he say hello to us?' grumbled Suzuki.

'I dread to think of the money he is going to say I owe him, when he does.'

'Haa, money! I like him to say hello,' insisted Suzuki.

'I'm glad he doesn't.'

'Ludi San is nice, I think.'

'He's nothing of the sort,' said Mary closing the subject.

But why didn't he come? If only he would. These days, no one but Captain Tanaka walked up the track to the house.

The Police Captain was becoming desperate. Antipathy against, and desire for this American woman were causing a fermentation in his mind, threatening his work, his life. Impossible now to allow a day to pass by without climbing the mountain track. If duty held him to his desk, he would become confused, and the longing to be 'up there' would become intolerable.

He would make excuses to his subordinates, excuses he knew

were too futile to be taken seriously. They knew he was lying – and why. He was an afflicted man, and, if this kept up, he would be demoted. The swaggering pride his position had always given him now mattered not at all.

That woman. Her fine gold hair, long slender legs! If he closed his eyes at any time her face would appear before him. He had stared so often at her face that he believed he knew the number of eyelashes fringing the strange foreign eyes.

The almost bare cupboards in her house were more familiar to him than those in his own home. He would remove everything from them, lingeringly handle her sparse supply of underclothing. She would sit watching him in silence, showing no interest.

Squatting on floor-cushions, their knees almost touching, he would stare at and question her for hours; trivial questions, he knew. Her slightly husky voice answered unwillingly, and when she was speaking, her hands gestured delicately. Those hands! Was it the fact that those hands would never voluntarily touch him – was this why he vented his frustrations on them?

The bamboo cane he now used to punish her was more satisfactory than burning her with cigarette stubs. Cigarettes were hard to come by, and, indeed, there were so few places on her hands left to burn. With the cane, he could beat until his arm was tired. It sickened him that he had to beat the hands he longed to have caress him.

If only she would cry out at such times, implore him to have mercy, behave as a female creature should – but no! She sat, face contorted, sweat dampening her brow.

He had beaten the old servant for interfering. Nowadays he ordered her to stay outside during his visits.

One night, lying sleepless beside his wife, he had thought of a way to have those hands touch him, and he had trembled, tears had actually filled his eyes. To have her touch him!

With a dull wife and five children to support, it was seldom that he could spare even the small moneys that massage cost. The American woman would massage him, massage his body.

It had taken time, and many beatings, to make her try to do

it; but her hands would not obey, and victory would fade, lie at his feet in ruins, for she would begin to vomit as though contact with his skin had caused a germ to enter her.

At these times he truly hated her, desired nothing more than to find her guilty of an illegal act. Find a short-wave radio in the house, black market food – anything! He blamed himself bitterly for warning the German, Portuguese, or whatever Hoffer was, to keep away from her house. Any trumped-up charge that he might make against her would rebound, make a fool of him eventually. Now that the black-marketeer was out of the picture, he would never catch her out in anything illegal.

Truthfully, that was not what he wanted. The desire ruling his waking moments, haunting his restless sleep, was to possess – seduce. The thought of trying, and not succeeding, with the American woman did not bear thinking of. Would there be time? There must! He would master her – when? Maybe tomorrow.

7

DAZED and weakened by Captain Tanaka's inquisition, and by serious lack of food, Mary fell into a dreamlike condition of mental escape, the last resort of the helpless.

Sitting on the tatami floor, awaiting and dreading Tanaka's arrival, she made weak ludicrous plans to come to terms with him. Suzuki had gone to the village to see if food rations were available, and Mary indulged in her habit of thinking aloud, finding the sound of her own voice oddly comforting. 'I shall kneel carefully, hands placed just so, bow until my forehead touches the floor. I shall say, "Captain Tanaka, don't beat me any more, don't make me massage your body any more, don't sit and look at me any more . . ." ' Her voice now was shrill, imploring.

The figure of a man darkened the doorway. Ludi knelt beside her on the matting, shaking her gently. 'Mary – why, Mary!'

She put her head against his shoulder; his arms, warm, comforting, went around her. 'There, there! Nothing is as bad as all that.'

'Oh, Ludi – you don't know . . .'

'I do know,' he said, and soothed her as one would a distressed child. 'Be still, just be still.'

A haven of peace; to stay for ever, like this, at peace, to stay for ever . . . She became aware that he was shaking with suppressed laughter, and looked at him in startled amazement. 'You are laughing at me – don't, you shouldn't!'

'Not at you, at myself, for I came here today in desperation, for help, and now I find myself playing Puppa to an hysterical mess. Mary, I'm really desperate.'

'I also am desperate and for a moment I felt you understood, felt your sympathy . . .'

'I do sympathise with you, but today I have no time to play games. Tell me, how brave are you? How strong are you?'

This was a different voice from the teasing one she was accustomed to. Something must be terribly wrong. 'What is it, Ludi?' she whispered.

'How brave are you, Mary?' he repeated.

'I don't understand!'

'Answer me, have you a supply of courage? Is it in you to fight for something that could endanger your life?'

His fingers dug painfully into her thin shoulders. He was asking her to help, to fight, but her mind had been inactive for so long, too long. She closed her eyes to his demands. 'No,' she said. 'I can't fight – not even for myself.'

'I thought as much,' and as abruptly as he had arrived, he walked from the house. Running after him she called wildly, 'Come back, don't leave me. I can do what you want. I can, I swear it.'

He stopped for an instant, then, without turning to face her, continued on down the track. She stumbled after him, caught at his arm. 'I promise you, Ludi.'

'It's no use, Mary.'

'It is, it is!'

He looked at her intently, and suddenly he smiled. Mary, caught up in the brightness of that smile, felt that, no matter what was demanded of her, she could do it.

He led her further down the track to where, hidden in the bamboo grove, a rough handcart stood, heavily laden with cloth-wrapped bundles. 'What would you say is in that large dirty parcel?' Ludi pointed.

'Could it be that you have captured General Tojo?' she asked feebly, staring at the grotesque bundle.

He gazed at her in stern admiration. 'Do you mean to tell me that you can see it's a man? I've pulled that blasted cart along for two days, pulled it today along the main street of the village, and past the police station. The saints were with me, no doubt of that!'

'A man! Is he dead?'

'If he isn't, he soon will be. Come on. Help me.'

Together, they lifted the weighty clumsy load and carried it up the incline, into the house. With Suzuki's scissors, he cut through the heavy cords, and Mary beheld a sight that caused her to fall to her knees in consternation.

Pushing her aside, bending over the pitiable object, Ludi examined the man's condition with confidence and authority. 'He's alive! Bring hot water, soap, towels, anything you have. Have you any sheets?'

'No sheets.'

'Your cotton underthings, clean cloths. Hurry!'

She brought what she could, and running back to the little kitchen to boil water on the smoking fire, crashed into Suzuki, who looked at her brilliantly flushed cheeks in amazement.

'You are in a fever.'

'No. Suzuki San, come and help us.'

'Us? Which is us?'

'In there, in there.'

Ludi was working with gentle haste over the stranger's body. From the mouth of the unconscious man a thin stream of blood seeped slowly.

33

'I think a rib has pierced his lung. Poor cuss!' said Ludi
grimly. 'And one of his arms is broken. Suzuki San, get me some
sticks, to use as splints. Hurry! Don't just stand there – both of
you. Hurry!'
This was too much for the old Japanese woman. To see Ludi
in the house again after all these months; lethargic Mary, full of
energy and excitement, that was enough, even too much, but the
man on the tatami floor was a nightmare.
Picking up the shirt Ludi had cut from the man, an expression
of awe and disbelief on her face, Suzuki looked from the shirt to
the matted fair hair of the stranger. 'Hoor! This one is an
America soldier-san!' She threw the shirt from her in distaste.
'Don't be ridiculous, Suzuki San,' cried Mary. 'Get the sticks,
do as Ludi says.'
'She is a smarter girl than you,' said Ludi. 'Move, both of you,
do what I say.'
Mary did as he commanded, but Suzuki, going to the cupboard
where she kept a treasured old brown bag, began to pack her few
belongings, muttering as she worked.
'You are going from here?' asked Ludi.
'Going,' she replied firmly.
'Hurry up then, old one, and if you even think of what you
have seen here today, I shall come and kill you. Kill you bad.
Understand?'
'I just go, no talk, just go.' She came closer to Ludi. 'Why you
bring trouble to Mary Sama? Why you come here? Better you
stay away.'
Picking up her luggage, back bent with haste and distress,
Suzuki left the small house, and went slowly down the hill
towards the village.

34

8

WITH a blunt knife, Mary hacked away at the silver birch tree, her thoughts as clumsy as her actions. How shall I manage without Suzuki San? I can't . . . but no time to think of that now. The stubborn branch broke away from the tree. Take it inside. Hurry! Kneeling beside the injured man, Ludi spared her a fleeting glance. 'He must have a doctor.'

'We can't trust anyone, you know that we can't.'

'He *must* have a doctor.' Ludi passed a hand over his face. 'Bring me a bundle from the cart, one wrapped in a purple furoshiki, some things in it we can use, and make sure that the cart is completely hidden. It's heavy, but you'll have to manage – somehow.'

Heaving, pushing and shoving, Mary managed to move the cart into hiding among the bushes. Then, breathing heavily at the unaccustomed exertion, and hearing footsteps hurrying up the track, she stood rooted to the ground, as firmly rooted as the trees about her, and watched Suzuki approach, bag held baby-like in her arms.

The old woman called, 'Tanaka! Tanaka come behind me. Quick! Let's be in a hurry!' and she ran ahead of Mary into the house.

As they burst into the room, Ludi's eyes met those of Mary, and they knew that Tanaka's arrival spelt doom, not only for the man on the floor, but for themselves. They stood looking hopelessly at the circumstances which made a perfect trap for Captain Tanaka to catch them in.

'Upstairs. The attic! Put him in the attic, Ludi Sama!' cried Suzuki.

'And the mess? The blood on the floor? The muck?' groaned Ludi.

'Suzuki fix!' The old woman began to throw the clothing and boots of the stranger into the cupboard from which she had so lately removed her own things.

Ludi and Mary lifted the unconscious American soldier. They hoisted him across the floor, and up the narrow, ladder-like staircase, as though he were a sin that they wished to hide from the eyes of God, while the strident voice of Tanaka demanded admittance at the front door.

Slithering down the stairs, Mary intended to attempt to remove the bowl of bloody water, and the towels that were seeped in blood; but she watched with horror, as Suzuki, taking scissors in gnarled hand, pulled the grey cloth of her kimono up to disclose a pathetically thin pair of old, very bandy legs.

Competently and savagely Suzuki cut gashes in her own flesh; blood welled from the wounds, and she uttered a strange sound of pain and fright, but mostly of satisfaction. 'Cut my legs in woods,' she hissed, sloshing soiled towels into the already blood-stained water.

9

CAPTAIN TANAKA was at once aware of something different. Suspiciously his eyes took in the alert, flushed appearance of Mary Ogata. What had caused this animation, this breathlessness?

The servant! She was in a bad state. He unbent a little, for there was something valorous about the old woman as she sat attempting to staunch the flow of blood from her leg wounds. 'You should be more careful, old woman,' he said, after hearing her tell of how, in the woods, she had fallen and injured herself on the sharp branch of a dead tree.

'Sharp as a ho-cho – sharp as kitchen knife,' earnestly repeated Suzuki.

'If you didn't demean yourself working for this American woman it wouldn't have happened. Why don't you see the error of your ways, and find work among our own people?'

'So! You may be right. I have been lately feeling this myself.'

Virtuously, pursing her lips, she continued mopping at the blood on her legs.

Captain Tanaka was bitterly disappointed, for with the injured old servant in the room things could not possibly be as usual. He would leave, come back tomorrow. Impossible! He could not drag himself away. He would stay for a while, at least hear Mary Ogata's voice.

Her replies, usually so unwilling, today fell from ready lips. Strange! She was saying more than was necessary. Puzzling! The very air in the room was puzzling. He placed his hand on Mary's knee. She had not flinched, not drawn back, not even noticed his hand? Something *was* amiss. Something very strange had taken place.

He increased the pressure of his hand. Ah! That was better, a long shudder. If only the servant were not present. If only . . . He rose to his feet. 'I shall examine your kitchen today. Your face speaks to me of black-market food.'

The kitchen! No good food had been cooked there, that was obvious; he returned to the room. 'I shall now examine your cupboards.' He would hold her clothing in his hands; they were a part of her.

This was routine to Mary. Accustomed to his going through her belongings, her indignation had long since faded. But – today!

Captain Tanaka slid the cupboard door aside, and Mary's cry rang out as the boots and bloodstained clothing fell to the floor at the astonished policeman's feet.

He gathered up his treasure and looked triumphantly into the eyes of the American girl. Then, throwing the clothing down, he began systematically to search the room.

Nothing! He stood in thought. His eyes went to the attic stair, and, crossing the room with a few quick paces, he put his foot on the first step.

'*No!*' said Mary, and picking up the scissors she plunged them deeply into the blue serge of Tanaka's back.

In shocked agony he turned to face her. The scissors, seeming to have a life of their own, stabbed into his face, into his eyes.

37

Was this agony his? That high screaming voice, was it his? Again and again the scissors plunged, as he fell to the floor. 'That's enough!' commanded Ludi, coming down from the attic. 'That's enough – I'll finish him. . . .'

Ludi and Mary, breathing deeply, looked at each other in complete accord.

'You must hide dead body,' said a weak voice.

They emerged from their trance. Suzuki, her wise old eyes heavy with trouble, repeated, 'Hide dead body.'

Ludi spoke briskly. 'Mary, clean up the mess. Get Suzuki San into bed, we don't want her on our hands, as well as Snooks upstairs in the attic.'

'Is that his name?' She felt that her voice was coming from far away. 'Is that his name?' she repeated, as though the man's name were of the utmost importance.

'Tom, Dick, Joe – I don't know what his name is. Do as I say.'

'Yes, of course – but what are you going to do?' Mary stood helplessly.

'Look for a place in the woods where I can take and hide Snooks; I'll wrap the remains of this too inquisitive policeman in the same cloth that I used for the other, load him on the cart, drag him through the village, dump him as far away from here as I can.'

As he spoke, Ludi was busy with the body of Tanaka, wrapping it first in charcoal-bags that he had found in the kitchen.

'His blood is seeping through – get me anything you can, to wrap him in, but nothing that could be traced to this house.'

'If you move the American, he will die,' said Mary.

'You would say that! Do you want the police to find him here when they come looking for Tanaka, as they will. It's well known that he comes here every day. I've even heard it said that he is your lover,' Ludi grinned.

'Why, you . . .' Mary choked with anger. Even at a time like this, he could joke.

'Get on with the work. No! Stop what you are doing, help me

38

lift your boy-friend here; he's trussed and packed as well as I can manage.'

Between them, they carried the remains of Captain Tanaka down the track. 'Poor cuss,' muttered Ludi.

'How can you say that?' She was glad that Tanaka was dead, and was beginning to feel a peculiar pride in what had happened.

'He was doing what he thought was right, what he'd been trained to do. Most men can't do more than that.'

Dumping the body on the cart they returned to the house, Ludi carrying a rucksack with him. 'Treasure this food, ration it out as cleverly as you can; I don't know where the next lot will come from – and now, I know of a place to hide Snooks. It'll have to do until I come back. If I never come back, it'll be up to you to keep him hidden!'

'You will come back though, you will . . .'

'I'll be back. Snooks here is a kind of insurance to me.'

'Insurance?'

'Yes, the war will be over soon. I'll stand in high with our conquering Yankee heroes if I can produce him alive and kicking.'

'You are much more heartless than – Tanaka. Than anyone I ever knew.'

'But you haven't known many people, have you? Help me again, you high-minded creature.'

They struggled with the living burden, carrying him out of the house, up the woodside, to a thick mossy shelter among the trees.

'Come here every hour through the night, and see how he is. On no account move him. If he regains consciousness, don't speak to him, just give him small spoons of the cognac that you'll find in a vinegar bottle in my rucksack. Give Suzuki San a little of it, too. Don't forget.'

Once more in the house, Ludi went over the place like a bloodhound, removing every shred of evidence that anyone but Mary and Suzuki had been in the house that day.

Bundling up clothing, bloodstained cloths, and the straw, he made them into a rough parcel. 'I'll get rid of this,' he said, and bending over Suzuki, he spoke softly. 'Good-bye, take care of yourself. You too, Mary, and wish me luck.'

After he had gone, Mary once again went over the house to see if he had missed any clues. Finding none, she went to the rucksack, and taking out the vinegar bottle, raised it to her mouth. The brandy made her throat tingle; she wanted to drink the whole bottle, drink to the last drop. Forget the world.

'Don't forget me,' cried Suzuki San firmly.

10

LUDI dragged his cart down the main street of the village. Before the war this had been one of the most delightful streets in the Orient. Branches of famous shops in Yokohama and Tokyo had opened there for the summer, selling pearls, silks and curios. Coffee shops and beer-halls had overflowed with carefree people.

Today, the shops were boarded up, and the people, walking aimlessly, looked as though they too had been boarded up. The only cheerful voice to be heard was Ludi's, as, pulling the ramshackle handcart along after him, he called greetings to everyone he met.

Coming to the wooden barrack-like police station, he propped the handles of his vehicle against the steps of the building, and strolled inside. 'Konbanwa.' He said good evening to the young, hungry-looking official, who sat going through an immense pile of papers.

The distraction was a relief to the man. Looking up from his work, he saw who it was and grinned. He had received many handouts of tobacco from the black-market dealer. 'Ah, soo! It is you, Hoffer San.'

'Dull work you have to do?' smiled Ludi.

'Yes, but it has to be done. What do you want, Hoffer San?'

'I want to see Captain Tanaka. I have a complaint to make to him.'

'A complaint?'

'Yes, I left my cart down by the railroad station today; when I got back to it, someone had stolen my rucksack. It had most of my clothes in it, but, more important than that, my mother's photograph, the only one I have of her. My mother is dead, and I want it back, I must have it back. When will Captain Tanaka return? Cigarette?'

He offered a packet of old and stale 'Bat' cigarettes to the man, who accepted one thankfully.

'So nay! Captain Tanaka should have been here at least one hour before this time. I wish he would hurry. I should have been at home some time ago. He is a punctual man, I cannot think what has kept him.'

'Is it all right if I wait in here with you?'

'Certainly, all right.'

An hour passed slowly by. Ludi longed to smoke again, but dared not let the man see that he had a good supply of the hard-to-get luxury. They chatted in a desultory fashion, in Japanese.

'Your Japanese is excellent, Hoffer San. I wish I could also speak English as well as you do Japanese.'

'I have a talent for speaking foreign languages. The secret is to be cheeky, for if you are scared of making a fool of yourself, it's hard to learn.'

'Ah! Is that the secret? Then I am afraid I shall never excel,' laughed the policeman. He looked at his wrist-watch, a worried expression on his face. 'Tanaka San *is* late, very late.'

'I can't wait any longer, it is getting dark. Will you be kind enough to tell him about my mother's photograph? Tell him I know it may not seem important to him, but . . .'

'Even Tanaka San loves his mother,' smiled the man. I shall tell him. Thanks for the tobacco.'

'Don't mention it.' Going out into the darkness, Ludi picked up the shafts of his cart and began to pull it down the main street. Away from the village.

11

THAT was a sleepless night for Mary. Her mind buzzed with an exhilaration that she had never felt before. Towards midnight she returned from her third trip up the dark slope. The injured man lived, but there was no movement except the shallow rise and fall of his chest to show it. 'Who are you? Where did you come from?' she had murmured. 'Will you ever speak to me?' There was no reply except for the sighing of the wind in the pines.

In the house Suzuki slept in deep exhaustion. Removing the food and other articles from Ludi's rucksack, Mary put them into the cupboards. Then she went out into the dark woods, and buried the bag itself in a hole in the ground. In her thoughts she was following Ludi and his dangerous cargo, through the village and far out along a country road to some place that he would know of.

What would she do if he never returned? To whom could she turn for help? Tanaka had forbidden her to visit the village. She knew nobody there, had no friends. She would need help, no doubt about that. The American airman needed a doctor, Ludi had said, and it was obvious. Also, and in the meantime, the police would undoubtedly come to question her about Captain Tanaka's disappearance. She would have to be calm and quick-thinking.

As dawn came, she heard footsteps approaching. She opened the door to a middle-aged well-dressed Japanese man, who was accompanied by a village policeman. 'Mrs Ogata?' asked the well-dressed man politely.

'Yes, what is it?' There was genuine surprise in her voice. This man, she knew, must be connected with the police. She had not expected a policeman to speak politely.

'May we come in, please?' The man's English was excellent, much better than that of Tanaka.

'Yes, but will you try not to wake my servant? She is ill, has just fallen asleep after a night of fever; she is old.'

'We shall try not to wake her, but it may be necessary to question her. Mrs Ogata, did Captain Tanaka call at your home yesterday?'

Beneath his quiet manner, Mary discerned a mind superior in every way to that of Tanaka. A new fear rose in her heart. 'Captain Tanaka?'

'You seem surprised at my question! I was under the impression that he came to visit you practically every day. You speak as though you had never heard of him.'

She seemed to hear Ludi say in a rough voice, 'It's up to you, lady.'

Calmly she replied, 'Captain Tanaka has come daily to my home for many months. I know him well, but he does not like me.' She hesitated. 'He seems to think that I am a spy.'

'Are you a spy?' asked the detective, in the friendliest manner.

'No, I am just a hungry and very tired woman.'

'Mrs Ogata, you have not answered my first question. Did the Captain come here yesterday?'

'Yes, he came, but he was different from usual.'

'Oh! In what way?'

'When he saw that my servant was ill, he said he wouldn't stay. I was surprised, for the Captain has never shown any kindness to this house.'

'How long did he stay?'

'About ten minutes. He said he would come back later, but he didn't.'

'You are sure of that?'

'I am certain. Did he tell you that he came here twice? It is not true!'

'He has not told us anything. Since he left the police station yesterday, to come here, he has not been seen or heard of.'

'Captain Tanaka?'

'Yes, the Captain is missing, Mrs Ogata. You realise of course that this is a serious matter, for he is a valuable man, a conscientious officer. Where do you think he can be?'

'I? How could I know? After he leaves my house he ceases

43

to exist for me, and I must tell you that the Captain frightened me, he . . .'

'Frightened you? What do you mean by that? That he will not frighten you again?'

'I don't understand.'

'You spoke in the past tense, Mrs Ogata!'

As Mary opened her mouth to speak, a moan came from Suzuki's bed.

'What is it, Suzuki San, are you feeling bad again?' Mary bent over her.

'Bring chamber-pot, quick, quick!' cried Suzuki. 'I need it bad.'

Knowing that there was no such utensil in the house, before going to the kitchen in pretence of obeying the old woman's demand, Mary asked, 'Surely you will excuse us for a few minutes?'

'More than a few minutes,' groaned Suzuki. 'Aarah! Never have I felt so bad!'

'We shall wait outside.' The detective spoke understandingly.

'Now you are becoming foolish!' hissed Suzuki. 'Now don't become foolish.'

'I don't know how to answer him. What shall I say?'

'Say little. Words are dangerous things.'

When the men returned the elder of the two said, 'We won't stay, we shall come back later, Mrs Ogata.'

'Yes, of course, if you have any more questions! But . . .'

He bowed politely. 'My name is Joji Noguchi, I am a criminal investigation man from Tokyo. If you recall anything, or if you can think of anything that could help us, you won't hesitate to let us know?'

'Certainly, but I have no idea . . .'

'Ah, yes! But I have found that people sometimes remember the strangest little things, as time goes by. Mrs Ogata, I shall send a doctor up to give your servant an examination, and to report to me on her condition.'

44

She was about to say that it was not necessary, when Suzuki broke into the conversation. 'Thank you, thank you – I am not worth the trouble. But, kekko – good. I need a doctor!'

When they were alone, Suzuki turned to Mary and said, 'One would think I were the one with the high learning, and I never went to school even one day in lifetime.'

'Did I do so badly?' asked Mary.

'Not bad – not good. Better lie down, Mary Sama, better sleep.'

'I must go up the hill again.'

'No need to go up hill, he won't run away. You sleep now, so you can go up hill later.'

In less than an hour Suzuki was shaking her and whispering urgently, 'Someone coming, someone is coming.'

'What? Who is it?'

A woman's voice was calling for admittance in the usual Japanese way, 'Gomen Kudasai.' Which means, 'I am sorry to disturb you.'

Mary slid open the door. 'I am Doctor Kimura.' The visitor spoke briskly, and bustled into the room. 'Where is my patient?' Her eyes were kind and Mary was tempted to blurt out, 'He's a little further up, in the woods.' Instead, she pointed to Suzuki, saying, 'This is Suzuki San.'

'Haa!' The doctor spoke enthusiastically. 'What ails you? I was told that you had a bad bowel upset. Now, tell me in your own way, for I never trust a man's opinion. I do not like men, have fought them all my life. First my father – what a hidebound man he was. Then the teachers at Medical School – what small souls they had. But I have triumphed over them at every crisis in my life. I have never married, couldn't bear the thought of having to live under the same roof with one of the conceited creatures.'

Mary and Suzuki looked at her in amazement, bemused by the flood of words.

Doctor Kimura examined Suzuki briefly and continued, 'You

45

are in fine condition. Maa! What a healthy old woman you are. Never married, have you?'

She crowed in triumph as Suzuki said meekly, 'No, Doctor.'

'I knew it! The havoc a man can cause to woman's health. You and I are two of the blessed ones.'

Suzuki looked at her incredulously. It was, to her, a great sorrow that no one had ever thought her important enough to arrange a marriage for her. 'It seems to me, Doctor, that you may have bitten into a sour apple somewhere along the line. I *regret* never having married!'

'Regret? Ridiculous! From this moment, change your thinking, appreciate your freedom. Now, I would like to hear the truth, please. What ails you?'

Stubbornly she awaited their reply. 'Come on, come on. The very air between us is thick with secrets. I am an old dog on the road. I assure you I can't be shocked.'

Suzuki spoke quietly. 'I have had an accident to my legs. I did not want the police to know, in case they insist that I be taken to the village for treatment.'

'Why should you be frightened of being taken to the village?'

'Not of that! I did not want to leave my young lady alone here at night. She is nervous.'

Doctor Kimura looked sternly at Mary. 'You, I take it, are a man's woman. Frightened of being alone!'

Mary burst into tears, the happenings of the past twenty-four hours overwhelming her.

'See what you have done now!' scolded Suzuki. 'Mary Sama is a brave lovely girl. If you but knew what a man has done to her – look! Look at her hands!'

Taking one of Mary's hands, seeing the havoc that Tanaka had wrought, Doctor Kimura drew in her breath. 'This confirms, only confirms, my stated opinions. Now tell me, ladies, do you know of any woman who could do a thing like this? Come on, now. Do you, do you?' she demanded.

When Suzuki bared her legs for inspection, the doctor once more drew in her breath. 'I shall have to stitch you up. It will hurt, for I have no drugs to numb your pain. The worst part of being a doctor these days is the shortage of . . .' Her voice trailed off as she began her task.

Before the doctor left, she looked thoughtfully at the two women. 'You are sure there is nothing else you wish to say to me?' From the bed Suzuki spoke with authority. 'We can never thank you enough for your goodness.'

'That's it, then. Nothing else?'

'What report will you make to Mr Noguchi?' asked Mary.

'Condition much improved.' Doctor Kimura thoughtfully closed her leather satchel, and bustled out of the house.

'What a woman!' Suzuki sounded exhausted.

'I liked her.'

'She is crazy. I do not trust her.'

'We should have told her about him, about the American,' insisted Mary.

'Tell that talk-too-much old woman? I do not trust her.'

'Maybe you're right, but the man will die if nothing is done for him.'

'Buddha! Christo! Ludi San and me don't want him to die. No one want him to die.' Suzuki hobbled to the kitchen. 'Mary Sama, take this rice-soup, it is good and thick, put a bit into his mouth. Ludi San say don't feed him, but do what Suzuki says. Men know little of sickness.'

'Have you changed your opinion of men so quickly?'

'Hurry,' ordered Suzuki, in an embarrassed voice. 'Hiaku.'

For two days no one walked up the track from the village. Suzuki was now able to visit the stranger. On stiff sore legs she made her way to him and hourly she forced small quantities of brandy and rice-gruel between his lips.

'The bleeding has stopped!' Mary spoke in delight, but Suzuki was deeply worried about the man's condition. His arm was swollen and ugly; fever burned in his body.

'Why doesn't Ludi come?' Mary cried.

Suzuki swore violently. 'If he don't come soon, no use to come

47

at all, and this boy will be dead and I want to know where he come from.'

'He must have fallen from one of the B.29s that pass over the village on bombing missions. He must have!' said Mary.

'Fall from "B." Land softly? Just break arm? Just get hurt?' Suzuki was scornful.

'Then where did he come from?'

'Only he can say,' declared Suzuki. 'If he ever say any talk again. That Ludi San is a bad one, to bring him here, and leave him with us, and not come back!' She added, fairly, 'But maybe Ludi San is caught. Maybe they caught him with that Tanaka – in the cart.'

'No!' cried Mary. 'Don't talk that way, Suzuki San. That would be too much.'

12

EARLY on the third day a policeman arrived. Mr Noguchi, he informed Mary, requested her presence at the police station. With a frightened glance at Suzuki, she left the house.

Arriving at the police station, she was startled to see Ludi Hoffer, sitting at his ease, looking well fed and confident.

Mr Noguchi greeted Mary gravely. 'Please be seated, Mrs Ogata. Captain Tanaka has, we are certain, met with foul play. He has not been found. We intend to find him. Mrs Ogata,' he continued, courteously; 'you still insist that you know nothing of this man's strange disappearance?'

'I know nothing.'

'Did Mr Hoffer call at your house that day?'

'No.'

'You are sure of that?'

'Yes.'

'But, Mrs Ogata! He says that he did.'

48

'He says he did?' Mary put her hand to her throat, to cover the pulse beating so sickeningly there.

'Yes, he said he had been to your home. That you had quarrelled – violently. He will not say why you quarrelled, and so I have asked you to come and tell us. It is strange that you forgot to mention such an important happening.'

Her mind was blank; not even the shadow of an idea came to her, it was impossible to speak.

'You must tell us, Mrs Ogata!' Mr Noguchi spoke normally, but to Mary his words came as from a great distance.

Ludi said glumly, '*She* won't tell you. I can't stay here all day, so I shall tell you.'

'You have delayed long enough,' agreed Mr Noguchi. 'But I also can't stay here all day. So, continue, Mr Hoffer.'

'She has been sleeping with me for the past six months. I have paid her with cigarettes and with food that I have been able to forage from the farmers . . .'

'Aah.' Noguchi spoke softly.

'The day, that day, I had been unable to bring her anything. We quarrelled. Now, no man likes to think that price is the first consideration . . .'

'She does not appear to be that kind of woman.'

'I thought that myself, but I was mistaken.'

Mr Noguchi turned to Mary. 'Is this true, Mrs Ogata?'

'It is true,' she whispered, playing her part.

Mr Noguchi's sympathies were with Mrs Ogata; he would give her time to compose herself. 'Mr Hoffer, sit down, please. There are a few things I would like to clear up about you. May I see your papers, please?'

Ludi readily produced his papers. Mr Noguchi read through them rapidly.

A flicker of interest came to Mary. She knew nothing of Ludi's background.

'Born Shanghai. Father, German. Mother, Portuguese. Arrived this country 1942. Occupation, business man. These papers tell so little. It is always the way. I dislike paperwork.

49

Now, Mr Hoffer, would you tell me how you have lived here in Japan for two years and more, doing no work? Where did you get the money to live?'

'I brought it with me. Made it on the Shanghai Dollar-Yen black-market exchange. It's lodged in the Yokohama Specie Bank. Quite an amount.'

'Amazing! Did you intend to settle in Japan with your ill-gotten gains? You don't mind my enquiring? I am intrigued.'

'Stay here? Certainly not! I intended to get out as soon as I could, but there was no way. I wanted to go to the United States, but you know how impossible it was to get priority.' Ludi said this as though speaking to a friend who cared deeply about his life's ambitions.

'And so?'

'And so, I came up to this village when the bombing became bad in Tokyo. I have my mother's nationality; I am a neutral; you know that.'

'Yes, I can imagine that you would manage to be neutral in any war.'

'I am a man of action, I can never sit around doing nothing, so I have dabbled a little in the food market. The police here know all about that.' Ludi smiled slyly across the room, to where two young policemen stood with their mouths agape. 'I think that I have supplied them with most of the food that has kept them in such good condition. Rations are poor, aren't they?'

'Yes, the rations are poor,' murmured Mr Noguchi. 'Mr Hoffer, did Captain Tanaka buy any of your black-market goods?'

'Never. I always feel, though, that he knows that his boys indulge a little. It can't be a crime for them to put food into the mouths of their children. I don't care what anyone says, I think that any father who could pass up a chance to get a bit of food to feed . . .

'Please! Mr Hoffer, don't become so heated. You are evidently fond of children. You speak as though you believe that Captain is still alive?'

'Of course I think he is still alive. Don't you, sir?'

Mr Noguchi sighed. 'I am beginning to doubt. You took your mother's nationality? May I ask why? It is not usual, is it?'

'My mother was not usual, either. By the way, has anything been done about finding the person who stole my rucksack? I want that photograph back.'

'Nothing, as yet. You were saying?'

'My mother was the daughter of a rich and well-known family of Macao. My father, a German business man from Cologne, died when I was small. I grew up with my mother; we were very close; she was beautiful. When I get my picture back, I will show her to you, I adored her, she . . .'

'Thank you. Mr Hoffer, did you see Captain Tanaka that day?'

'If I had seen him I would tell you. I like Tanaka, and I think I can safely say also that he likes me. We have a kind of understanding. Ask your men here how he feels about me?'

Mr Noguchi turned to the men. 'No, I won't ask them,' he said. 'They could really give me only one answer after your remarks about the black-market.' He began to laugh. 'I would like to have you on my staff, Mr Hoffer, but I am afraid that I would find myself working under you before long. Now, I ask you in all sincerity – is everything you have told me here today true?'

'All, except for Captain Tanaka liking me. He hates my guts; I have to tell you this, because he'll tell you himself.' Ludi looked directly at Mr Noguchi and smiled.

After a moment, Noguchi nodded decisively. 'I see! Thank you, Mr Hoffer.'

'Do you want me any longer?' asked Ludi. When told that he could go, he lounged out of the place, ignoring Mary completely.

'You, also, may leave, Mrs Ogata, but I may have to see you again. Please be ready to come down here at a moment's notice; I must clear this serious matter up. I am sorry about all this.'

And he did appear to be sorry.

51

13

THAT night, Suzuki and Mary again visited the sick man. 'Arm is very sick, stinks bad,' muttered Suzuki.

'It's gangrene; he will die soon, I know it – we can't just let him die. Why doesn't Ludi come and do something? He is a louse!' said Mary, desperately.

'Police watching him maybe. He will come, but looks like going to be too late.'

Just before dawn Ludi entered the house and without greeting them, said, 'I have brought a doctor, she's with the man. We'll need your help. You boil some water, Suzuki San. Mary, sterilize those scissors; we are going to amputate his arm, it's stinking to high heaven.'

'With the scissors?' Mary pressed her hands against her stomach.

Ludi looked at her in exasperation. 'Not with your scissors, but we want everything that we use to be sterile and we may need your murder weapon to cut bandages. Just do as I say.'

'Why did you take so long to come, Ludi? You should have come before this!'

Spreading a large canvas sheet on the matting, ignoring her questions, he left the house and returned, carrying the injured man, accompanied by Doctor Kimura, who immediately glanced at Mary. 'Send that girl away,' she ordered, speaking fluently in English.

'She may be needed,' Ludi objected.

'Never! She has no nerve,' answered the doctor. 'But we need the old woman.'

'Mary can watch the path.'

'No need to watch the path. What we are doing cannot be hidden at short notice. Tell that young woman to go up the hill, and clean up the mess there and not to come back till we call her.'

Ludi jerked his head towards the door and Mary obediently

went up the hill. With her fingers she roughened the pressed ground where the wounded American had lain; then she sat, waiting to be called, hoping that they might, after all, need her.

Doctor Kimura worked with skill and precision. As she worked, only necessary words fell from her tight lips. Suzuki watched her in admiration. When the doctor had put the final stitch in the ugly bloodied stump that remained, Ludi rolled over gently on the floor.

'Maa! I can't believe it!' exclaimed Suzuki. 'He's fainted!'

Doctor Kimura spared but a fleeting glance for her defeated assistant. 'Men! Give him a dose of the brandy; we need him, he has strong muscles. Let us also take a dose of the stuff.'

'Do you think that this man will live?' Suzuki asked.

'If he doesn't, Fate is strange. He seems to have been through more than most people could live through, and he still lives – who is he?'

'I don't know.'

'How did he get here? Does he come from the village? Why didn't you tell me before that he was here? If he dies, you are maybe to blame. I could have helped him better then. Did the American girl stop you from telling me?'

'No!' Suzuki answered gruffly. 'I stopped her – *she* wanted to tell you.'

'She did?' the doctor looked surprised. 'Well! Are you with us once again?' she demanded of Ludi. 'We need you. Come on, let us finish what we have started.'

'Mother of God!' moaned Ludi. 'Do you have to talk so much?'

'Talk? Certainly. Call the girl; she can help us now – we need her to clean up – and where shall we make my patient's bed?'

'Don't call the girl, I'll clean up; and we don't make any bed up. He must be moved away from here!' Ludi held the brandy bottle to his mouth; it was now more than half empty.

'Moved? Never! Not my patient.' Doctor Kimura narrowed her eyes, daring Ludi to go against her.

'The police will come here. If they find him . . .' Ludi ran his fingers across his throat.

'Hoor! So? Tell me the exact story. I can't be shocked. This old woman, Suzuki San, knows that I can't be shocked. You know that too. Come, tell me.'

Ludi spoke harshly. 'I found him lying in the forest fifteen miles from here. Don't ask me where he came from. He was dressed in American Airforce clothing – crumpled up – bleeding like a pig.'

'Go on. What an adventure! How did you bring him here?'

'Tied him into a bundle, put him on a handcart, and took two days dragging it here; Mary took us in. A police captain, Captain Tanaka, came to the house. To prevent him causing trouble, we killed him. We will do our best to kill anyone else who gets in our way.'

'Killed him! Killed a policeman?' gasped Kimura.

He looked threateningly at her, and she returned his look admiringly. 'My, you are a bold person!' Straightening her shoulders, she announced with confidence, 'But I allow no boldness, no interference whatsoever, with my patients. This man has become my patient. I think only of his welfare.'

'If we leave him here—' Ludi began.

'No if. I don't know that word. He is here, and here he stays, until I say otherwise.'

'Then – in the attic?' suggested Suzuki.

'Is there an attic? I shall examine it!' Agile as one of the squirrels in the walnut tree outside the house, Doctor Kimura scuttled up the stairs. Her gnome-like face appeared looking down into the room. 'This is good. We shall carry him up here tomorrow.'

'He must be out of sight today.'

'Young man! He stays where he is until I, Kimura, say.'

'Buddha! Christo! How you all come to be in this house?' complained Suzuki.

'Soo! Enough of your talk, everything is settled. To work! Call the girl!' The doctor began to tidy up, talking incessantly. Ludi and Suzuki gazed at each other hopelessly.

54

'Now,' continued Doctor Kimura, 'bury the limb deep in the ground. Hide it well.'

As Ludi carried the grisly object out of the house, she turned to Suzuki, and demanded, 'And you! Where are you going?'

'Just going outside. You are clever, I am not, but I know enough not to talk all the time.' Suzuki put on her wooden sandals. She was on her way up the hill to see Mary.

The doctor shrugged her shoulders and laughed. 'These people are different; even the servant gives orders. I feel quite bucked up by the whole affair.'

Ludi was already digging. Suzuki stood beside him, and said hesitantly, 'Ludi Sama!'

'What is it, old one?'

'Do you trust that one?'

'The doctor? Certainly not, and so I am going back to the house in a few minutes, to frighten all the confidence out of her.'

'You can do that?'

'Yes, I can do that.' He wiped a dirty hand over his face. 'Suzuki San, will you do something for me?'

'Can I?'

'Yes. Make a bath in the old wooden tub in the kitchen.'

'I can, I will. But first I call Mary Sama.'

'I'll call her.'

'No, I call her.' She plodded stubbornly uphill.

Returning to the house, Ludi found Doctor Kimura sitting beside the sick man. She had removed her horn-rimmed glasses and her face now appeared guileless, quite old. He hesitated, regretting that he must speak unpleasant words. She'd done a fine job, but he said quietly, 'Let us talk a little, Doctor Kimura.'

'No talk, I must have quiet, please.'

'There is great need to talk. You are the doctor, but I am Boss Man around here; you must realise that.'

'In this case, I am the boss.'

'You are only the doctor. Now! I chose you, Doctor Kimura, above all the many doctors in the village; there are many, as you know – German, French . . . They probably would have been glad to do what you have done here today, and done it just as well,' he added, as Doctor Kimura gave him an annoyed look.

'Then why did you come to me?'

'Because I know so much about you.' She now gave him a startled glance.

'You practised secretly in partnership with a foreign doctor, who is now in Sugamo Prison, and he will be there for many years. Now, Doctor Kimura, I don't want to upset you, but I want you to know that if you act against our interests, and if you don't help us here, in our strange trouble, to your full ability, then I shall, at the first opportunity, inform on you!'

'You could not hurt me.'

'I could ruin you, and you know it well. Abortion is not practised in wartime Japan; it is a major crime. You know it, I know it, and neither of us wants the police to know it, do we?'

'How do you know about me? I do only what I think is the right thing. I am a disciple of Doctor Sanger. The population of my country . . .'

'Lady, lady!' Ludi laughed softly. 'I agree with you. Have we reached an understanding? You help us; we protect your good name?'

'We, you and I, understand each other.' Biting her lower lip, she looked steadily away from him.

'That's right!' Ludi entered the small steamy kitchen, where Suzuki stood waiting to scrub his back. He stripped the soiled clothing from his weary body and burrowed under the water. Only a few bubbles showed that he was in the tub.

14

DR KIMURA, a rapt expression on her face, squatted beside the patient. The smell of chloroform, the hushed atmosphere of the room, sickened Ludi. He glanced from the doctor to Suzuki, who sat, Japanese style, heads nodding as old women's heads nod the world over when weary.

They looked like two nice old Buddhas. Who wanted to spend a summer evening with two female Buddhas? Life, no doubt about it, was a lousy business these closing-in days of the war. It was bound to end soon. Japan had already reached the bottom of the barrel; he was certain of that, and it couldn't end soon enough to please him.

He yawned long and loudly. Suzuki's eyes flew open, and stared at him in disgust. Kimura stuck her chin out, the look on her face branding Ludi a serious offender against sickroom etiquette.

He refused to be intimidated, and as Mary, fresh from her soapless bath, tying a red sash about a faded cotton kimono, entered the room, he grinned at her and winked.

She too gave him a prim, shocked glance.

There was Mary! Reminding him of a hovering butterfly, as she stooped over the ill man on the floor. What a waste! Butterflies lived on honey. No honey there for her. What kind of girl was she? He had never fathomed the reason for her, to say the least, unusual marriage. Mary, in the arms of a Japanese man – any man – a surprisingly distasteful thought. Why the hell should he care in whose and how many men's arms Madam Ogata had lain?

He *was* in a bad way, it would be better if he went outside, left the women to watch and care for Snooks. But how unbearably prim Mary looked. No girl so tantalisingly lovely had the right to look at him in that manner, as though she were his maiden aunt. Why should he stand for it? He wouldn't.

Mary, amazed to find herself lifted and carried to the garden in Ludi's arms, held her breath until he dumped her unceremoniously on the grass.

'Ludi, you're crazy! What's wrong with you?'

'Yes, I'm crazy – bored, tired and crazy. I like the way you Americans use English. It's crazy. Let's *be* crazy, just a little. Huh?'

'Really, Ludi!'

'No? You're a born spinster, Mary. Have you ever, once in your life, abandoned your important little self? Lived for the moment, as they say, I believe, in the classics. Have you?'

To be like him – able to forget fears past, present and future, not to think of tomorrow! For the briefest moment she relaxed.

'Aa-haa!' Ludi caught at her hand. 'Wonderful!'

Wonderful! Did he suppose she was another – what had he called the Chinese girl? – 'Quite a dish!' What an ego he had; how impossible he was, how could he forget, even for a second, the trouble they were in – how dare he?

'No?' Ludi lay back, hands behind his head, and grinned up at her. 'Take your hands off your hips, Mary. A girl in a kimono, even a faded one, must never stand like that.' He laughed softly.

'You're impossible! Ludi, how can you forget our troubles even for a second? How can you feel so easy?'

'How can you not? Go away, Mary, you bother me. Any man born of woman would be bothered; moonlight, summer air, a girl, arms akimbo, standing over, *glaring* down at him. Mary – go – away!'

He rolled over, buried his face in the grass.

She sat beside him. 'Ludi, I wish that I could be the way you are.'

'What! You still here? Aren't you afraid of the night air?' Was that tiny sound, that sniff, the beginning of tears? He sat up, and looked at her. She *was* crying.

'Mary, I can't bear tears; I was only teasing, you know that! Cheer up!'

'I'll cry if I want to. I feel like crying, and I'm damn well crying, not because of your teasing as you call it, but because even at a time like this you can play and joke and I can't. Now shut up!'

'Quite a fire-ball! Did you say you are crying because you are not like me? Like *me*! As Suzuki San would say, Aaarah Maa! How surprising.'

'Why don't *you* go inside—' once started, crying was wonderful, refreshing —'and leave me to cry?'

'Cry away! Enjoy yourself.' He walked towards the house. She would call him back, for no woman could bear to have a man walk out on her tears.

'Ludi, please come back and talk to me.'

He laughed. 'I'm here, what do you want to talk of? Take these.' He handed her a handkerchief, a comb and a lighted cigarette.

'So self-sufficient. You're like a department store, Ludi. What else have you in your pockets?'

'A curiously unladylike question and one to be ignored. Feel better?'

'A bit.' She drew the smoke deeply into her lungs. 'Ludi.'

'What is it now?'

'Oh – I don't want to bore you. It's nothing really.'

'O.K. What a night – just look at the moon, isn't it a beautiful night . . .'

'Yes, a beautiful night.' How casually uninterested he was in her. 'Ludi, when I said I envied you, I meant that I envied you your self-confidence, the way you face life. If I'd had a better father, if my mother had lived, I might have been like that too; but my mother died when I was born, my father—'

'Yes, you've told me about your old man. I know all about that, but what do you mean – if your mother hadn't died? What has your mother got to do with a big girl like you?'

'She would have loved me, helped me grow up the way your mother helped you. When I heard you saying to Mr Noguchi, "I grew up with my mother – we were very close – she was beautiful" I felt jealous, I really did.'

What was Mary gabbling about? He had better set her right;

59

the truth would maybe jolt her, but it's always better to speak the truth. 'My mother was quite famous . . .' he began.

'And beautiful, you said,' she interrupted.

'Beautiful? She may have been once. Her name was Ria; she was a prostitute. I've seen her thrown out of the lowest dens and dives in Shanghai.'

What was he saying? She should have known that it was impossible for him to be serious with her. Just let him carry on with his craziness . . .

'Certainly I grew up with her. Many a cold night she put me out of her room, left me to sleep in the gutters with other beggar kids. That woman loved her job, put her whole self into it. Some dame, my mother! Have you got the matches? Thanks.' He lit his cigarette. 'When I was small I took her for granted. She was Mamma.'

'You're lying, Ludi, and I don't know how you can lie about a thing like this, about your mother.'

Was there a man living, who would lie about a 'thing' like this? Mary was so childish. 'Maybe I'm lying. I have a vivid imagination. Take the story you heard me tell Noguchi, take this story that I have told you, then take your choice. To continue, and I'm going to continue because I'm very human, and humans adore talking of themselves. There's nothing better than an audience listening to the unique story of oneself.'

'I don't want to hear about you; I'd rather not.'

'You don't want to listen? But you would like me to listen to your story? Too bad! I've listened to you many a time. Now, let me tell you of *my* father.'

'No, I'm going to see how things are inside the house. You are hateful!' But she did not go, and he went on with his story.

'My father was a German seaman. He lived with Ria one whole month. "One whole month Hoffer stayed with me . . ." I've heard her bragging, putting her friends in their proper places many a time. In her circle, it was quite something to know a client's name, but to have him stay a whole month was a triumph.'

As though soliloquizing, he continued, 'At fourteen I got

60

myself a job in the Cathay Hotel, bell-boy. I loved that clean job; I'll never like any job the way I liked that one. It didn't last long, though, because the Manager asked me, "Aren't you Ria Hoffer's kid?" I should've known better, but I said "Yes, she's my mother." '

"What did he say to you, Ludi? What did he do?'

'He said nothing. Made a fist of his hand, thumb jerking out towards the door. I got for my life. It happened again, and again, so I gave up. No decent place would employ the son of the city's most notorious foreign tart.'

'Didn't you ever go to school?'

'Yes, the Jesuits took me for a while, but I ran away, because the other kids knew about my mother. I read everything I could lay hands on, I used to collect the newspapers, English, French, Chinese. I spoke different languages pretty well, it's easy for a kid to pick up languages he hears; they all seem one. Later on in life I found out they were different and that I spoke no less than five languages fluently.'

Surely his story couldn't be true? But one never knew with Ludi. . . . 'You speak Japanese well, much better than I.' She would be casual, grown-up about the whole thing, just in case he was teasing.

'Japanese! I learnt that language from the Japs when they took Shanghai over. I was grown-up then.'

'How did you get to Japan? How did you get your money over here?'

Ludi laughed, and rose to his feet. 'That's another story. I wouldn't tell anyone living that story. That money means a lot to me.'

'It must. What became of – your mother?'

'She died in the streets she lived in.'

'You took care of her, I know you did.'

Soo! Mary insisted on frosting the cake. 'I did not!'

'I'm sure you gave her money.'

'Certainly I gave her money, everyone gave her money, it was the quickest way to get rid of her, she smelt bad.' He was silent

61

for a moment, and then, catching at her hand, heaved her lightly
to her feet. 'Well, Mary, which story is the true one?'

'I . . .' Her voice trailed into silence.

Well, it was a raw story, even watered down. How far off those
Shanghai days seemed tonight. How he'd despised his mother,
resented the dreadful pride she'd had in being the mother of a
son. Over and finished with now, buried – to be forgotten. Mary
was the only person who would ever hear from him the story of
his life.

Why the hell had he begun all this? There was a nasty taste
in his mouth. What was she saying, and how darling she was in her
kimono.

'Ludi, if what you've told me is true – I'm sorry. I had a
lonely childhood, an unloved one, but . . .'

Of course! Mary and her self-pity had started him off. 'Neither
of us had much of a childhood, Mary. I don't believe that
matters, for it's either born in you to be something, or it's not.'

'You may be right, I suppose you are, but I find it hard not to
resent my father. Don't you hate and blame your mother?'

Ludi spoke lightly. 'Blame my mother? Hate my mother? I
adored her. When I get her photograph back I'll show you how
beautiful she was.'

'But? Then everything you've said has been a lie.'

'True! Untrue! Mary, it doesn't matter. Can't you get anything into your head. I am myself.'

She laughed. 'I don't understand you but I admire the way
you get things done and . . .'

'Was that a laugh I heard? It was the nicest sound I've heard
for ages. I hate sombre dark things and people. Laugh again.'

Had she laughed? Surely she hadn't, and she certainly couldn't
laugh to order.

'Mary – laugh?'

'You are crazy, I'm in no laughing mood and you shouldn't be
either. Don't you realise how . . .'

Ludi caught her swiftly to him. She *would* laugh, he wanted to
hear her again. Girls were made to laugh, to love. Was she

wearing anything beneath her cotton kimono? It felt not, and for all her talk she seemed to have no objection to being held like this. Could it be that she was wanting what he so desperately wanted? Find out! Touch her lips with his fingers. It was like touching a clinging petal. How long since he had felt like this? Strangely enough, never before, quite like this. . . .

Suzuki came running from the house, calling out as she ran, 'Come quick! He is awake. He is making talk! Ludi Sama, hurry!'

One day, not tonight, but one day, Ludi decided he would get even with Suzuki San. He ran ahead of her into the house. Mary, feeling strangely at a loss, followed slowly.

15

MICHAEL PETERS had been raised in a fine home, in a fine American city. The only really not-nice thing that had ever happened in his twenty-four years of life, had been baling out of a blazing B29 over Japan. Hearing the gurgling sound that Bud Willis made as he died, feeling the warm splash of blood, Bud's blood, squirt over his face. Then the jump, pulling the parachute cord, and realising that this was it – the end!

In the deafening roar he had found time to regret that death, meant for old men, was claiming him. The mad descent, agony of lungs as they expanded beyond endurance. The parachute not opening properly. Falling, falling, dying. Yes, it's opening – too late? And now, how strange that in the end it should be like this.

Everything upside down! Those dark floorboards over his head? He opened his eyes a little wider, with great effort. The boards were the ceiling, and peering down at him were two gnomes, one wearing horn-rimmed glasses. He shut his eyes, tried to make his mind work.

Name? Michael Peters.

Serial number? What was the number for? The war! The

bombing mission! His buddies! The flames! The . . . But – he was dead! No? Then what?

Too great an effort to open his eyes again, he listened very carefully.

'Sss – Pssss. Ssssss.' What was that sound? Someone talking? Could it be birds? No. Then – Monday! Mom has Mrs Miata, the Japanese laundrywoman in the kitchen . . .

Mrs Miata! Japanese! The gnomes were Japanese, he was in Japan. Not dead, not home.

He tried to move his lips; they were so light, not there; he tried again, a sound came from them. His eyes opened again, more easily this time. One of the gnomes spoke; her voice came from far away, up in the sky somewhere. 'Gooda boya,' she said proudly.

Into darkness again. A hand touched his forehead, and he heard a man's voice say, 'He's coming to.' A hand, warm and strong, in his, a voice, warm and strong, saying, 'O.K. . . . O.K. . . . Now . . . You're safe. O.K. now.'

'May I – sleep?' whispered Mike.

'That's a good idea,' answered Ludi.

'Stay with me?'

'I'll stay with you.' Ludi's hand tightened just a little on the remaining hand of the young American.

Hours passed by. Dr Kimura packed her bag and left, saying that she would return later.

Mary and Suzuki crept around in the room as silently as mice, 'Mary Sama, take blanket, go down watch track. No sleep tonight,' whispered Suzuki.

Stumbling down the steep rough path, Mary felt that she would be as ineffectual in guarding the track as the sleezy blanket she carried would be in keeping out the rain that began to fall. She settled down to wait and listen. Would Dr Kimura give information to the police – if so, what then?

In the house, Suzuki opened wide all doors and shutters. Using the precious stock of kerosene, she wiped it over the matting floor, and poured the last drops on the kitchen fire. Smoke fumes filled the air, and gradually the faint sickly odour of chloroform faded. From his crouching position alongside the patient, Ludi grinned at her approvingly.

Suzuki came from the kitchen with a steaming bowl of rice-gruel, and kneeling beside Ludi, she held a spoonful to his lips. Unwilling to speak, he made a hideous face of refusal, but she held the spoon firmly, fed him to the last sticky drop. Then, an expression of satisfaction on her tired old face, she knelt behind him and massaged the kinking cramps from his shoulders.

Drenched and weary, Mary returned to the house, to find Suzuki fanning the fire under her precious black-market rice-gruel. 'Still asleep,' hissed Suzuki. She tasted the rice judiciously, nodding her head with satisfaction.

'May I have some? I'm starving – I really am,' begged Mary.

'Rice is for him,' whispered Suzuki. '*You* take that!' She pointed to a piece of cold sweet-potato. Mary took it, and stuffing it into her mouth, crept in, to stand watching Ludi and the ill man. They were exactly as she had left them hours before, except that, now, they were both asleep.

'You go back, go back and watch track,' coaxed Suzuki.

'No,' answered Mary. 'You go, I am tired.'

'I am better here than you. Mary Sama, go back and watch. Be gooda garl.'

Mike sighed deeply; simultaneously Ludi's eyes flew open and he frowned Mary and Suzuki out of sight as the young man awoke and spoke fretfully. 'Who are you? Am I ill? Where am I?'

'You are in a house in a Japanese village. I found you, in the woods; you were hurt. I brought you here. I am your friend, there are many like me in the village.'

'What's wrong with me?'

'Very little that can't be fixed,' said Ludi quietly. 'Easy now, take it easy – everything is fine, just fine.'

'It is?'

'Yes,' replied Ludi. 'Just fine.' He beckoned to Suzuki. 'Here is a Japanese woman, a friend, she's cooked some food for you. Come here, old lady. See! She can speak English. Say hello to him, Suzuki San.'

Kneeling down, holding the steaming rice bowl, Suzuki politely said: 'How are you?'

'Fine,' whispered Mike.

'Finer after rice,' Suzuki said sternly.

'Where's the other one?'

'That was the doctor, she's gone home, but Mary's here. Mary's an American girl; she's been taking care of you too. Come here, Mary.'

'I'm Mary.' She smiled down at him, and, taking the bowl and spoon, began to feed him carefully.

Rising to his feet, Ludi went to the kitchen and splashed his face with cold water. His alert ears caught the sound of footsteps far down the track. Fear welled up, his quick mind pushed it away, and he went back to the room. 'What's your name – tell me quickly?'

'Michael, Michael Peters.'

'The police are coming to question us, Japanese police, you know. Now you must help *us*!'

'But – how?'

'By keeping quiet. I'm going to lift you; it'll hurt, but I'm lifting you, to hide you in a cupboard.'

Ludi gathered Mike in his arms and crammed him into the wall cupboard. Sliding the door shut, he repeated, 'Quiet! No matter what. You understand?'

'O.K.,' Mike murmured.

Ludi pushed Suzuki into the kitchen. 'Be careful, old lady,' he whispered as voices were heard at the entrance and Mary was shocked to see that he was laughing. 'Strip off!' he ordered. 'Get into the bed, take your clothes off – all of them. Hide them in the bedding – they're wet.'

'I won't. Why should I?'

Still laughing, he pulled her blouse over her head. 'It's the only way, Mary.'

It *would* be the only way! Protestingly she removed her clothing, and crawled into the bed.

'Make way for me,' grinned Ludi. His clothes lay on the tatami

66

in an untidy heap. Lying beside her, he pulled the covers snugly over them both.

'This is monstrous!' stated Mary flatly.

'Ain't it just, tho'? I've got to stop laughing, I must be serious.' Rising on his elbow, he gazed deeply into his bedmate's unfriendly eyes.

'Mary,' he whispered in an impassioned voice.

'What?' she snapped.

'Crazy?'

He was rewarded by a giggle, the first girlish giggle that he had ever heard from Mary. 'Now,' he whispered sternly, 'you behave yourself.'

Another tiny giggle. 'Sssh!' Ludi covered her mouth gently with his hand.

She closed her eyes. Crazy indeed and yet how peaceful – a moment's shelter from storm.

Ludi was breathing as though he were deeply asleep, and Suzuki, passing through the room, threw a complacent glance at the bed. No cosmopolitan dowager ever welcomed guests with more aplomb, as, sliding the door open, she smiled at Mr Noguchi and his subordinate.

'Is your mistress awake?' asked Mr Noguchi.

Suzuki, now looking flustered, bent her head. 'My mistress is not yet awake. Could you perhaps remain outside? I will arouse her. We have but one room, as you know.'

Mr Noguchi, examining his compatriot with acumen, stepped past her into the room.

'Mrs Ogata, I apologise for this intrusion . . .'

Ludi, rising from the bed, picked up his trousers and hastily stepped into them.

'What is it?' asked Mary, sitting up, the blanket held about her shoulders.

'It's all right, Mary.' Ludi brazenly invited Mr Noguchi to sit down.

'No. I prefer not to embarrass further.' The detective backed towards the door.

'You couldn't!'

'I beg your pardon?'

'You couldn't embarrass further,' grinned Ludi.

'Oh! You must think me obtuse. Mr Hoffer, please step to the garden with me.'

'Suzuki San!' bawled Ludi.

'Hai, yes?' responded Suzuki briskly and brashly.

'Have you any tea?'

'A little.'

'Then bring it to us in the garden.'

The men stood in the glazed beauty of early morning. 'The quintessence of the day,' murmured Mr Noguchi. 'Dawn is the best hour, don't you agree, Mr Hoffer?'

'No,' said Ludi. 'I prefer the blazing light of noon.'

Mr Noguchi smiled. 'I see you, rather, in the "dark of the moon." Trivial talk is pleasant, but takes us nowhere,' he continued. 'I came to inquire from Mrs Ogata if she knew of your whereabouts, for you have not been to your room at the Inn for several days.'

'What do you want of me?'

'I have something for you.'

'I can't imagine what it is.'

'But you were so anxious.' Mr Noguchi looked expectantly at Ludi. 'Your mother's photograph!'

Ludi rubbed a hand over his unshaven chin. 'Of course,' he murmured.

'Of course!' repeated Mr Noguchi, delightedly. 'I now have it for you! Please call at the office for it today. And please ask Mrs Ogata to come with you. Oh! And offer her my apologies.'

Mr Noguchi began to walk down the track. Turning, he called, 'Come at your favourite hour, midday!' He beckoned to the waiting policeman and they went down, towards the village.

Mary, watching from the window, expected Ludi to bounce into the house and in spite of their problems to make something of the fact that they had lain naked in the same bed. Why did he just stand out there? Life stood still and an infinitesimal drop of warmth entered her heart. For those few moments in the bed beside Ludi she had felt safe, protected. That was strange, and although she dreaded the way he could reduce her to inadequacy, she felt the need to be near him again, and went out to the garden.

'Ludi.' She spoke his name hesitantly.

Shaking his head as though to clear it, he replied, 'Noguchi says that he has my mother's photograph. It's impossible! I've never even seen a picture of my mother.'

Running into the house, he called: 'Get a move on, we've things to do.' Suzuki, on her knees at the opened cupboard, was holding a bowl of hot tea to Mike's lips. 'You angel,' Ludi praised her. 'Are you O.K., Mike?'

'Yes.'

'I'm going to lift you out. Then, I'm going to make this cupboard your permanent home.'

'It's too short,' objected Mary.

'I'll take down the partition, make one cupboard from the two small ones.'

When Mike was lying once again in the middle of the room, Ludi spoke in admiration. 'You have great fortitude. He's a brave man, isn't he, Suzuki San?'

'Mike San got plenty gutz,' stated Suzuki proudly.

'I feel pretty bad really,' Mike murmured. 'What's wrong with my arm in the bandage – it hurts.'

Now! This was going to be hard – better to give it to him straight. 'Sorry, Mike,' said Ludi. 'It got gangrene; a doctor had to cut it off, to save your life.'

The young man *did* have guts!

'Huh? O.K. I can take it. I have to, I guess, but I feel mighty bad.'

'The doctor should be here soon; can you hold on?' asked Ludi, anxiously.

Suzuki brought the vinegar bottle. 'Give drink to Mike San.'

'Brandy! That's right!' Ludi raised his voice as Mary entered the room. 'Hide it from Mary, she's a dreadful drunkard.'

Mike gulped greedily and whispered weakly: 'Sit where I can see you, Mary.'

'She's pretty,' said Ludi, 'but an awful flirt.'

'Shut up! Get on with enlarging the cupboard.' Mary smiled gently at Mike.

'Yes, get on with my cupboard,' said Mike. 'Mary and I are going to flirt.' He fell into a fitful doze.

Regretfully Ludi woke him, and lifted him into the enlarged cupboard. When its doors were open Mike's cubicle was part of the room, but when the doors were slid shut he would be in stuffy darkness.

'What a risk you folks are taking for me,' whispered Mike.

'As soon as you are stronger and able to move about, the risk won't be so great.' Ludi spoke glibly. 'The war's nearly over. There's a village near here, ten minutes' down the mountain; the denizens of said village are the cream and the scum of Japan's foreign community. We can easily hide you among them.'

'Easily?'

'Well, maybe not easily, but it's possible,' Ludi grinned. From his rucksack he brought out a pair of much-worn corduroy trousers, a shirt and sweater, various other articles of men's clothing, and shaving gear. 'Mike, you'll have to eat a lot, and grow fat, if these things of mine are to fit you. We'll destroy what remains of your American uniform.'

Giving the bundle to the servant, he added, 'Mary, wash your face and comb your hair.' She looked at him in surprise, and Ludi said to Mike, 'Mary and I are going to the village for a stroll. Come on, Mary, your life's a mad gay whirl – from one man to another.'

Mary and Ludi went down the mountain track, and walked through the village street to the police station, to keep their noon appointment with Mr Noguchi.

16

MR NOGUCHI had ordered his lunch at the Inn to be ready at
noon. A frugal meal of bean-curd soup, thick with seaweed. He
took his time eating it. Raising the black lacquer bowl to his lips,
he sipped slowly, and, with ivory chop-sticks, skilfully fished for
the slippery dark-green balls.

He was, he always liked to think, a man of judgment, but the
Tanaka case was proving him not to be so.

That American girl! It had been impossible for him to believe
that she would prostitute herself. Noguchi could as well have
imagined his own daughter Yuriko, his one precious child, falling
to such depths. And yet with his own eyes, that morning, he had
seen Mrs Ogata in bed with that German-Portuguese. His
judgment had let him down. His career and reputation had been
built on his uncanny judgment.

He finished his meal, washed his hands, and, as he carefully
dried them, wished that he had embraced another profession.
'Art critic, theatre critic . . .' he mused, as he walked slowly over
to the police station to keep an appointment for which he was,
exactly and purposefully, one hour late.

Mary and Ludi had been sitting there waiting in uneasy
silence. A rotund young policeman sat with them, picking his
teeth, and carefully wiping the toothpick on a folded tissue. 'The
louse must have had some food to eat; doesn't it make you
envious?' muttered Ludi. The pretence that Noguchi had made
about the non-existent photograph of his mother had him
seriously worried.

'Choto! Come here!' he called authoritatively to the policeman.
The man looked at him sluggishly. 'Hai? Yes?'

'Bring this lady something to eat.'

'There is nothing here to eat.'

'There is always something to eat.' Ludi produced three
cigarettes and a glint came into the man's eyes. Shuffling over to
a cupboard, he brought two white rice-cakes to Mary.

'That's worth two cigarettes. Hot tea, and you can have the other,' Ludi snapped.

'Hai.' Going to the small charcoal brazier, with a tattered fan he began to bring the kettle to boiling-point.

'Eat the rice-cakes, Mary.'

'How nice they look, like snowballs. One each, Ludi.'

'They're both for you.'

'I couldn't eat, while you have nothing.'

'Do as I tell you,' said Ludi wearily. She dug her teeth into the succulent, salty cakes, and ate both of them ravenously.

'Noguchi San is coming. Give me the cigarettes, quickly!' The policeman placed a cup of steaming green tea in front of Mary and took his payment.

'Ah, tea!' said Mr. Noguchi. 'Two more,' he ordered. 'You have missed your lunch through my tardiness.' Sitting at his desk, he examined a small file of papers. 'Saa! Now, that is better? Tea is good. I am sorry to have kept you so long.' Taking the top paper off the file he handed it to Ludi. 'Your mother's photograph, Mr Hoffer.'

There was nothing pleasant in the haggard face of the woman that looked up at Ludi from the photograph. He stared at it with incredulous horror.

'Mr Hoffer, may I have your attention?' Noguchi spoke quietly. 'Mrs Ogata, kindly hand me that photograph.'

As she rose to obey, Ludi spoke. 'Don't look at it, Mary.' He handed the photograph back to Noguchi, who smiled and said, 'It is your mother?'

'It was my mother.'

'You seem amazed?'

'I am amazed.'

'Mr Hoffer, I do not admire shock tactics, but I have used them to prove to you that your delusion in thinking that I am a village policeman is incorrect. We, in Japan, have ways and means. I have here a dossier on your mother, her police record. Would you care to see it? You figure in it slightly.'

Ludi shook his head.

'Ah! Perhaps not; I sympathise with you, for I am Japanese and I know that, without pride of family, man has but little.'

'Where did you . . .?'

'Obtain my information? It was simple. Shanghai is our territory. These papers are of no value to me, except to provide me with knowledge concerning the strange disappearance of Captain Tanaka.'

Ludi remained silent. Noguchi waited.

'Knowledge?' asked Mary at last.

Noguchi sat back in his chair. 'The knowledge that Mr Hoffer is a liar.' Turning, he bowed to Mary. 'I have concluded also, Mrs Ogata, that you have also lied to me. I am going to find the truth.'

'Haven't you found Tanaka yet?' asked Ludi, now seemingly self-confident again.

'Not yet,' answered Noguchi quietly. 'But I am sure that his body will turn up soon. It is reasonable to believe that he is dead.'

'Why would anyone murder Captain Tanaka?' asked Mary brightly. Both men looked at her in astonishment, Noguchi also in beaming delight.

'You ask the very question I wish you to answer,' he cried. 'Will you give me the answer to your question, Mrs Ogata?'

'He's not dead,' said Ludi stolidly. 'Most likely cleared out! Other men have done it – I have done it. . . .'

'Ah. You, perhaps! Tanaka, never! He liked being a policeman, he enjoyed it.'

Ludi stood up and stretched his strong body. 'I could name a dozen people in the village who have a grudge against the man,' he said. 'Tanaka could possibly be in difficulties.'

'Soo?' interrupted Noguchi.

'Tanaka is an uneducated tyrant, a product of Japanese bureaucracy; he misuses his power, he . . .'

'Sit down,' said Noguchi.

Ludi sat down.

'I am not interested in your impudent opinions, Mr Hoffer.

Tell me instead why you called here on the day of Captain Tanaka's disappearance? Tell me the reason for your call, and for the rigmarole of lies you have told me? From now on you will confine yourself to answering questions.'

'I could send you on many a wild goose chase,' Ludi grinned.

'I think not,' answered Noguchi. 'Why did you come here on that day that Captain Tanaka disappeared?'

'To get my money from him!'

'Go on,' said Noguchi, sternly.

'Black-market is big business. Over thirty people are concerned in this district alone. I could give you the names!'

'I want no names. Just continue your "story."'

'We have a system. It is dangerous to meet openly, so I allow the money owed to me to accumulate, and then it is placed, on a certain date, in a certain part of the woods, and I pick it up.' He paused again.

'Go on.'

'Tanaka found out. He watched, waited his chance, and picked up my money, a large amount of money – my money.'

'Your story now begins to verge on the ridiculous, Mr Hoffer.'

'Money is never ridiculous,' said Ludi, 'I had to watch him walk away with it. I came here that day to make him pay me.'

'And he didn't turn up?' said Noguchi forlornly.

'You know damn well he didn't turn up,' said Ludi angrily.

'Why?'

'I don't know why, that's not my pigeon. But I can, if you want me to, give you some advice.'

'Yes?'

'Why don't you search his house, question his wife? If the money is not found there, you can, if you believe me . . .'

'I do not believe you, Mr Hoffer.'

'Let us assume that you do for the moment. If the money is not found, Tanaka has cleared off with it – vamoosed.'

'Ridiculous!'

'If the money is found in his house, I also will believe that he is – er—' ended Ludi flatly.

'You exhaust me.' Noguchi took off his glasses, and placing his fingers at the corners of his eyes he massaged gently.

'I can give you another lead,' said Ludi. 'Seriously, I can help you. Question a man named Usami. Tanaka was after one of his daughters, a pretty girl, about seventeen. I used to sleep occasionally with his elder daughter. We did a lot of business together; nice old chap, Usami,' said Ludi reminiscently. 'But he never allowed anyone to touch the young one. I know, I tried, and was badly scolded. Tanaka raped the young girl. She died in premature childbirth.'

'Mr Hoffer, please . . .'

But Ludi's flood of words flowed on. 'The old man was bitter. If he'd had a gun he would have killed Tanaka.'

'You are sure of this?'

'Yes. He asked me for my gun.'

'You have a gun?'

'Yes.' Ludi produced a small pistol and placed it on the desk in front of Noguchi.

'Domo!' Noguchi could not conceal his amazement. 'Quite against the law.'

'I have no ammunition,' explained Ludi. 'If I had, I would have given the gun to my friend Usami.'

'And he could have shot Tanaka, and we wouldn't be in all this trouble?' said Noguchi, inanely.

'That's right,' laughed Ludi.

'I do not believe a word you have spoken. You do not delude me.' Noguchi rose to his feet. 'You may go now. Both of you – but do not leave the village, Mr Hoffer.'

'O.K.,' said Ludi.

'Where will you be staying? At the inn?'

'I shall be at my girl's place. I shall be with Mrs Ogata.'

'I see.' The elderly man looked over the top of his spectacles at Mary. 'Mrs Ogata, where is your husband?'

'He is in Tokyo.'

'What a pity,' commented Noguchi.

Mary and Ludi walked back through the village. When they

75

came to the turn in the track, Ludi sat down, and Mary sat beside him. 'He knows that we killed Tanaka,' she said despondently. 'He knows nothing of the sort!' said Ludi. 'He thinks, maybe, that we did it, but not knowing about Mike, the clever old boy is at a disadvantage.'

'He didn't believe a word of your story. What a fool you were, adding lies, lies and more trouble to us all.'

Ludi laughed. 'He didn't believe me, but he couldn't get rid of us quickly enough to get started on the wily trails I set him.'

'Wily trails! I never heard such stupid flagrant lies.'

'Nearly everything that I told him was true.'

'Stop it!' Mary jumped to her feet in anger.

Ludi caught at her hand. He laughed. 'It wasn't true that Tanaka took the money, but it is true that Noguchi will find it in Tanaka's house, for I hid it there. You just don't realise how subtle I am.'

'I certainly don't. But the other story – the one about the farm girl?'

'That's really true, and I can't claim any credit for inventing it. Tanaka did rape old Usami's younger daughter.'

'But now Noguchi will arrest that innocent old man . . .'

'No,' said Ludi. 'Noguchi can't do that.'

'Why not?'

'Because Usami San is dead and buried these past four moons.' Ludi crossed himself dolorously. 'But Inspector Noguchi will investigate, and he will find out that I gave him some reliable information.'

'There's no doubt about you,' said Mary, admiringly. 'And he will also question the elder sister, the one you were so very personally friendly with!'

'Oh, her! Bit of an upset will do her good, take some of the fat off her bottom,' Ludi laughed.

'Vulgar, as usual. Well, it's understandable, when one remembers your background!'

He caught her arm roughly. 'It doesn't matter a damn to you what my background was, or what kind of man I am. But it matters to me, and to Mike, and to Suzuki San, and even to Doctor Kimura, that you stop being stupid.' He shook her. 'Who would want to murder dear Captain Tanaka?' he mimicked. 'Noguchi was delighted to hear you suggest that word murder. From now on, stop being a fool.'

He gave her a little shove, and walked on ahead to the house.

17

SUZUKI appeared to have aged during the hours they had been away, and her voice was distressed. 'Kimura San not come yet; Mike San much hurting.'

'He must have a sedative,' Ludi proclaimed. 'One of us must go and bring the doctor.' He looked at Mary. 'Not you, you might botch it.' Turning to Suzuki he said, 'You will have to go, old lady.'

Taking her outside, he directed her to Kimura's house. 'Return quickly, don't waste time.'

'Legs are *very* short,' said Suzuki. 'I leave this house.' She spoke in Japanese, and Ludi responded, 'I await your return.'

Mary was kneeling alongside Mike, holding his hand. 'Mike, poor Mike . . .' When he groaned she made comforting sounds. 'Just a little longer. Suzuki has gone for help; just a little longer, Mike . . .'

Suzuki returned alone, carrying a small parcel. 'That doctor, she say, not coming, she sent this.' Opening the parcel, they found a roll of dressing, a piece of laundry soap, and a small bottle, containing white tablets.

'One every four hours,' directed Suzuki solemnly. Taking out two of the tablets, Ludi gave them to Mike, who, within ten minutes, slept soundly.

'You girls sleep, I'll watch the track,' said Ludi.

'No. You sleep. I watch the track a little,' Suzuki declared. 'Then I wake you.'

It was morning when Ludi opened his eyes. Mary lay curled up on her mattress. He looked down at her and wished that she could wake to a peaceful world.

There was an improvement in Mike's appearance, and Ludi felt rewarded when he heard him say, 'Hi there! Are you going to shave today?'

'Sure am,' answered Ludi.

'This damn beard is worrying me. Can you spare a blade?'

'You shall have first go.' Ludi prepared for the job. Stylishly making a froth of bubbles from the strong soap Kimura had included in the parcel, he lathered it on the thick beard. 'Brother!' he said. 'This is going to hurt you more than it will hurt me.'

No one came near the house that day. Mike lay half drugged. The other three waited on the alert.

Night fell, and still no footsteps came up the track from the village.

18

WHEN he found the bulky bundle of Yen notes in Tanaka's house, Mr Noguchi felt as though he were taking leave of his senses.

He went by bicycle, to visit the run-down farmhouse belonging to the Usami family. The only people at home there were a very old woman and her granddaughter Mariko, plump, smooth-skinned, and the brazen way she claimed acquaintance with Ludi Hoffer caused Noguchi to catch his breath.

He learnt that the master of the house was dead, and he was nauseated at the delight Mariko took in telling of the rape of her young sister. 'It was the policeman that did it. Oh, no doubt about that! Come – I will show you the very place!' The way young sister had screamed! She and the old one had not dared to interfere. Who, these days in Japan, would interfere with a police captain? Certainly not she, nor her grandmother.

Father had been desperate when he had been told – indeed, very desperate. But for all his wrath, what could he do against Captain Tanaka? Complain to the police, perhaps?'

She laughed. 'Tanaka San is – the police.'

On his trip back to the village, Noguchi decided to put the entire matter out of his mind until he had taken a bath. He would have to begin the whole case again from the beginning. Something was lacking; he must discover what it was.

'Two wild-goose chases already,' he murmured in English, climbing into the refreshing warm water of the tub.

That night he refused to let his mind dwell on the Tanaka case. Instead of that, he spent the sleepless hours worrying about his wife and daughter in Tokyo. So dear to him, so important. Without them, there would be nothing.

Here he was safe in this unbombed village. The enemy, the Americans, knew that it was populated, indeed over-populated, by non-Japanese people. The climax, the end of the war was at hand, defeat lay in store. Noguchi had always known that the outcome would be defeat. He hid his face in the unpleasantly soft pillow.

On the day after his return from the Usami farm, Mr Noguchi wrote down all facts of the case known to him.

The uncanny disappearance of Tanaka.

Mrs Ogata's 'out of character' behaviour.

The timely illness of the old servant.

Money, hidden but found so easily in the Tanaka home.

Farmer Usami! There was a man who had a deep grudge against the police captain. But – dead these many months.

The cynical attitude of Hoffer – not that of a man who would commit a crime of passion. It was extremely unlikely that Hoffer would have murdered a police captain through jealousy. There would have been some other motive – but what?

He added to his list the astonishment Hoffer had displayed

79

when Mrs Ogata had mentioned the word 'murder.' The man's astonishment had been genuine; no doubt about that.

Now! For what reason had the police captain been murdered? There had to be a reason for everything that took place in the universe.

Captain Tanaka had left the police station, walked through the village, climbed the steep mountain track and arrived at the house nestling up there among the trees.

Several residents of the village had unwillingly admitted having seen the captain on his way up to the house, but not one person had seen him return.

Noguchi decided to search that house. Around, about and under that house. If the body of Tanaka was not found there, then obviously Tanaka had come down from the mountain. When – and how?

He sat passively, eyes closed. Suddenly he found one of the answers to the puzzle. It was not so much his judgment that had been at fault; it was the fact that in this case he was dealing with foreigners. He had been thinking along the lines of Japanese thought, behaviour and action. Now he must think in another way!

Details of crimes committed in other lands flashed through his clear mind. He had a swift vision of Ludi Hoffer, cutlass in hand, cutlass dripping with blood, bravado on his bold laughing face – pirate ancestors! No doubt about that!

A man such as this Hoffer would not know the meaning of caution. Would most likely dare that which other men would perhaps hesitate to think, even dream about. Murder would be all in the day's doings for a man who had lived the childhood and young manhood of Ludi Hoffer, come out of it with colossal self-confidence, and with that big bank balance deposited in his name at the Yokohama Bank. Noguchi had inquired into, and had been amazed at the amount.

Soo! Tanaka had travelled down from the mountain house, pulled, or pushed along in Hoffer's handcart. Alive or dead? In all probability dead.

This deduction completely changed Mr Noguchi's plans.

No need now to search the house for Tanaka's corpse. He would follow the trail left by Hoffer that night, when he had left the police station pulling – or did he push? – the handcart laden with the dead body of a Japanese police captain. Some people must have seen him!

That doctor! That excitable, unwomanly creature, who had attended Mrs Ogata's servant – he would call and see her.

Just a moment! Deep in his mind he remembered a woman doctor? Had Kimura been the doctor's name? A woman doctor had been found innocent but suspect in a shocking abortion trial. Kimura! Could it be the same person?

With his uncanny sense he knew that he was right. He would see to it she behaved herself. There would be not much in her line of business to be done up here in the village. But then again – with foreigners one never knew.

The star actor in the Tanaka case, Hoffer, was certainly not curtailing his amorous escapades. Human nature! Strange, unexplainable and wonderful.

He allowed his mind to wander. What a pretty person Mrs Ogata was and how the bold handsome physique of the man had thrown her fair beauty into relief. Mr Noguchi was a student of the drama. He recalled with pleasure the virile man stepping naked, from the bed, and the ripe corn-coloured hair of the girl. Tousled by sleep? By the hand of her lover? The girl had sat up and spoken sleepily, the fears of the day not yet upon her. 'Aaah!' sighed Noguchi. 'I miss the American films.'

He felt that at last he was making some progress. He felt brighter, but a bright sun casts a dark shadow. Glumly, he realised that the crux of the case was still evading him, the *motive* for the murder!

He spoke aloud, as was his habit when quite certain that he was alone. 'I am convinced that something dark, unusual, something more important than the death by murder of a village policeman has taken place. I must search for the "happening" that led to the murder. That is what I must search for. I shall find it. It? Him? Her? For the time being – it!'

He would begin by giving the little house and its inmates a slight reprieve, that valuable police weapon – a false sense of security.

19

THE village hospital was a hive of misery. Dr Kimura stood at the bedside of her patient, an asthma victim, and longed for just one shot of adrenalin, to be able to give him even small relief. The doctors in the village lived in a state of perpetual anxiety, for drug supplies were running out; in most cases had run out.

A plain little Japanese nurse entered the room.

'What is it?' snapped Kimura.

'A man to see you.'

'I am busy.'

The nurse withdrew, to appear again in a few minutes. 'It is Noguchi San, from the police. He insists.'

'Insists! He can insist in his own domain, but *here* I am the one to take that line. Tell him I'll be free in ten minutes.' Kimura's mind buzzed with uneasiness.

After attending to her patient, she went unwillingly down the dark wooden staircase. Noguchi greeted her pleasantly. 'I am suffering from insomnia. Do you have something for me? Enough to give me one night's sound sleep?'

Much relieved, she said crisply, 'I have nothing for such a small complaint.'

'Ah! I feared just that,' murmured Noguchi. 'It must be hard for you doctors. No tools with which to do your essential work.'

'That is an understatement,' said Dr Kimura.

'How do you manage?'

'If you are really interested, just develop a condition that requires surgery,' was her scornful reply.

'Is it really so bad, then?' His voice was full of kindly interest.

That question opened a tirade against the dire shortages, the plight of suffering people in the village.

For ten minutes Noguchi listened sympathetically. 'Have you used up your private supply of sedatives?' he asked.

'Not all, not quite . . .' She hesitated. What a fox this Noguchi was!

'I thought as much. In your special line of surgical operations, keeping the patient quiet would be imperative. Don't bother to be indignant, Dr Kimura; I am aware of your illegal practices. Keep your sheets clean while you are in this village. And while I am here, I advise you to pay no more calls to the house of Mrs Ogata.'

'It was you who sent me there!'

'Now I am telling you to keep away.'

'May I ask why?'

'I have my reasons. You your orders. I wish you could have helped me with my problem.'

'Your problem?'

'Yes, my insomnia.' Mr Noguchi bowed. 'Sayonara, Dr Kimura.'

'I shall send you some sedative tablets,' she said, stiffly.

He walked thoughtfully up the hill towards the house of Mary Ogata.

Mary! It was a favourite name among Americans, apparently. When he was a little boy, he and his elder brother had been great movie fans. Silent films in those halcyon days, he mused nostalgically. His tall brother had dragged him along the street and into the dark of the little theatre. There, they would sit among their friends, watching wonderful cowboys shoot guns and ride jerky black and white horses. An interpreter had stood on the stage beneath the flickering screen, translating the story for them, calling all cowboys 'Robert,' and all the girls – who eventually ran into the stalwart arms outheld to them – 'Mary.'

Drawing near to Mary Ogata's house, he now glimpsed a running figure, but true to character he finished his 'memory.' I thought for many years that all American boys and girls were called Robert and Mary, he mused.

Now. Why is that old servant in such a hurry?

At the curve in the track, he noticed two fresh cigarette butts.

'Soo! They are keeping a watch!'

He walked rapidly towards the house.

20

FOUR days had gone by, without any unpleasant incident in the cottage. Suzuki had watched the reactions of her three housemates dubiously. It was good that Mike San was feeling so much better; he appeared to be improving hourly. But was it good to relax to the extent of, at times, hilarious talk and laughter? That Ludi Sama! His laugh was as big as he was; surely not necessary to be quite so bold.

She, Suzuki, was old and small; they, large and young. Should she follow their example, or should they take a lead from her? How deeply she was involved in this dangerous trouble! She, as loyal a Japanese as any, would gladly lay down her life, such as it was, for her country, if the necessity should arise. Had she done the right thing to remain with these people? If she had informed the police that an American enemy was being cared for, sheltered in the house, could she have faced her own inside-self again?

Good was good! Bad was bad! It would be bad to give this quiet, injured American boy into the hands of officials. He was a good boy, she liked him. She had done only what, to her, was the right thing. Soo! Carry on in the same manner, see the trouble through to the finish – no matter what. But these careless young people must be brought into line.

'Ludi Sama!' When he smiled like that, nothing to do but smile back, but she must be strict, swallow her smile, frown at him. Soo! He saw that she was serious.

'What is it, old one?'

'You like to eat after tomorrow?'

'I like to eat every day.'

'After tomorrow you can't eat. I am Cook San, and can't no Cook San cook with no food. You going to get some from somewhere?' How threatening she sounded.

'Suzuki San, have we so little left? Why haven't you spoken before? It was wrong of you!'

'Wrong, me? Not so. Wrong? You, yes. Talking, laughing at funny, when no true funny is in this house. Me, watching track, cooking rice, you eating, rubbing full stomach. Very nice for Ludi Sama. Very bad for Ludi Sama and everyone when tomorrow comes – yes? No?'

Like a small boy called in from play, Ludi Sama put on a sulky face. What was he muttering? Her ears were getting poor of hearing, he must speak up. 'What you are saying? Make a bigger voice.'

'I said I shall go down tonight. Do my best to get supplies.'

'Do best! Not so. Just get. Begin now. Maybe tonight things get bad again.'

'Bad? Oh, you mean that Noguchi might come?'

Hah! She had done what she'd set out to do. He was looking sensible again, worried too. Kekko! Very good.

There was Mary Sama, as gay as a lady entertaining two presentable men at cocktail-time. Suzuki had worked for families who had guests in for cocktail-time but it seemed a long time ago. What a weary passing of time this war was. What was it all about? She didn't know – Shigatakanai! It was Fate!

In her heart, she was glad that these young people had the spirit to throw off their worries. No one liked the party spirit more than she, who had never really been to a party. But she'd been on the fringes of many, and with her skill as cook, responsible for the success of countless parties. Here she was wandering hither

85

and thither, her thoughts affected by the careless atmosphere in the room. She must not be like a willow tree, swayed by the slightest breeze. She must not be like Mary Sama! Life's strong winds and little breezes did what they would with her. Now, Mary Sama had an unsuccessful 'Kimono-marriage' on her hands. And yet, no doubt about it, the girl was beginning to like Mike San. Not good – very bad!

Naturally any female creature *would* like Mike San. The room was dim, but the American's face was sunny, good to look at. Mike San – Mary Sama! Were they not too alike to make a good couple? Well, really! Who was she, Suzuki, to have such god-like opinions? Once again, Fate managed such things.

What did Ludi Sama think of the adoring attitude of the American girl to the American man? Was he noticing? He certainly was. Did he mind, did he want Mary Sama for himself?

She didn't know, but it could be Ludi Sama would never want a wife, and would always have a love affair on hand. No doubt about that. He was a man!

'I'll bring tobacco for you, old lady,' he was saying.

He certainly knew about women. 'Soo – yes. Try for my tobacco,' she said sternly as he went down the mountain path.

'Mary Sama, better you go watch at track,' she ordered.

'Me?'

'So – anata, you! Watch for police coming!' Maa! She *was* getting results. Only she and Mike San left in the house now. 'You lie down, Mike San. You take a time for little sleep.' Like a child he obeyed her. She certainly was in charge today.

In the afternoon, Ludi returned from the village with food and tobacco. He, Mary and Mike sat talking. It seemed that they never ran out of things to talk about. 'By this time,' Mike was saying, 'my folk will have heard that I am dead. I don't like to think of their suffering, but it will be fine, later, when they hear that I'm alive. I'm their one and only.'

'Me too,' said Ludi. 'I am an only child.'

'And so am I!' said Mary.

'Say, are you kidding me?' asked Mike, seriously.

'No, it's true,' they both said.

He looked at them doubtfully and changed the subject. 'My arm is healing like a miracle, I must be a healthy cuss.'

'You are beginning to speak like Ludi,' teased Mary.

Suzuki came hurriedly into the room. She spoke bitterly. 'Very nice to play at party. I make big noise coming up track. Noguchi San is coming behind me. . . .'

'Oh, God!' Mary jumped to her feet. 'What shall we do now?'

'Now, don't you start that!' said Ludi desperately.

21

As Ludi closed the cupboard door on Mike, he felt that there was hardly a hundred-to-one chance now of his not being discovered.

'I'll try to stop Noguchi from coming into the house.' He hurried outside. 'Ah, Noguchi San! Paying us another visit?'

'Yes. Where have you hidden the corpse of Captain Tanaka?'

Ludi glared at him. 'Are you mad?'

'No, Mr Hoffer. If there is a madman in this garden, it is not I.'

'Then there is no madman in the garden,' Ludi retorted.

The two men looked angrily into each other's eyes. Noguchi, furious that he could see no hint of fear in the face he was watching so carefully. Ludi, enraged that this policeman had the ability to shock him so drastically.

'We shall talk in the house,' announced Noguchi.

'Wait!' Ludi stepped in front of the older, smaller man. 'There is something I must tell you . . .'

Agilely, Noguchi stepped past him. Sliding the door open, kicking off his shoes, he stepped into the house.

Ludi followed. Mary and Suzuki sat on the floor, to all appearances halfway through a game of cards.

Ignoring Mary completely, Noguchi spoke rapidly in Japanese to Suzuki. 'Put your cards down, stop your game of pretence and tell me why you were watching the approach from the village?'

Suzuki answered slowly. Her listeners gathered each word she uttered as children gather rare shells at the seashore. 'I am a servant in this house. My mistress is kind, but I am still a servant. This man and woman do not want me always near them.'

'You lie. Stand up when you speak to me!' Noguchi shouted. Obediently the old woman rose to her feet.

He continued, 'What is hidden here in this house? Why did you run to warn of my coming? I insist that you tell me.'

'So? I often sit at the rock by the path. I can look over the village; it comforts me. Today, it is true, I did hurry back to the house. I remembered my cook-pot on the fire. My mistress has no skill for the kitchen. I did not hear you coming, sir. I am old, my hearing is not good, I am more than a little deaf.'

Noguchi turned from her in disgust. How was he to deal with these people? 'Mr Hoffer! Mrs Ogata!' he spoke now in English, and in his usual calm manner. 'Confide in me. Take me into your confidence. I know that you are in trouble.'

Receiving two blank glances he continued, 'Believe me, I know that Captain Tanaka has been killed. I know this. I also know that he was an unpleasant man, a trouble-maker. Tell me your story.' With a neatly folded handkerchief he wiped his damp brow.

'Mr Noguchi,' Ludi sat on the matting, 'I wish we could tell you something, but there is nothing to tell!'

'Nothing to tell,' echoed Mary, faintly.

Ludi spoke sympathetically. 'Have you visited the Usami farm? Have you searched Tanaka's house?'

Impossible man! He would ignore him. 'Mrs Ogata, I wish to be left alone in this house, I am going to search it. You, the three of you, leave me alone. I warn you to stay apart. I shall watch you.'

He was not feeling well. Once again he wiped his brow. Aah! The way they looked at each other, how unwillingly they left the room! The two women sat by the well. That Hoffer! Leaning there against the pine tree, as if he hadn't a care in the world.

Noguchi's intuition told him strongly now that here, in this house, was hidden that which he must find. What? And where to begin? Removing his jacket, he began to pry one of the heavy tatami squares out of its floor slot. This was hachi-jo, an eight-mat room. The squares were bound with heavy black braid, and fitted together with exquisite precision. Why was he doing this? How confused he felt – impossible to lift them! The war years had taken more from him than he'd realised. Hoffer could do this chore for him. 'Mr Hoffer,' he called, 'please come here!'

Ludi was blaming himself bitterly. Mike should have been taken to the village, passed from house to house. There were many people there who would have sheltered him. He must prevent the detective from opening that cupboard. No use standing inert under the old pine tree.

He reached the house just as Noguchi called his name. Was he too late? If Noguchi had already found Mike, it would be madness to interfere. There would be no sense in killing Noguchi; that was out of the question.

Surprise at seeing the cupboard door still closed on its thinly protected secret caused Ludi to bite into his lower lip; he sucked the blood into his mouth.

'Help me lift the tatami mats,' Noguchi ordered.

'Do you suppose that Captain Tanaka's body is under the floor?'

'Not his body that you took away in your cart, Mr Hoffer; but I may find, under the mat, some evidence that you have not been quite clever enough to hide. Some evidence of your motive for killing him. Just help me to lift this matting, please!'

'Mr Noguchi, your accusations are ridiculous!' With brute strength Ludi heaved up the squares, leaning them against the wall. 'There!' Get things over and done with. Let the Jap find the Yank! Why should he care? To have come through life as he had, such a tangled stringent life, to have come so far for this! He had no illusions about the fate that would await him if Mike were discovered – and Mary and Suzuki, too. The Japanese would have no mercy on any of them. Let the old bloodhound open Mike's cupboard. Finish the business. Clear out, run for it.

They stood amid the dusty untidiness of the uprooted matting, but the bare floorboards showed no secret. 'Do you want to lift the boards, too?' sneered Ludi.

Suzuki's voice interrupted. 'Mary Sama needs her handkerchee. May I get handkerchee?'

'Does she need to have it now?' asked Noguchi irately.

'Needs it. Nose is needing it.'

'Get it.'

Suzuki pigeon-toed over to the bedding cupboard, and slid the door wide open. Ludi stared incredulously at the pile of brightly-coloured sleep-mats filling the space where Mike should have been. The mats, which since Mike's advent had been piled daily in a corner of the room, now filled the entire lower portion of the cupboard.

The top shelf was as usual, with Mary's belongings neatly stacked on it. Noguchi glanced at some of the articles; he had seen them listed in Tanaka's diary.

Suzuki looked at him over her shoulder. 'Will you reach me that small blue box? Too high for my reach.' Politely he handed it to her. Carefully choosing a handkerchief, she trotted out to join Mary beside the well.

Ludi tried not to show his bewilderment. Mike must have left the house by the back door, got away into the woods, but no – he was too weak to walk many paces yet.

The kitchen? No hiding-place there. The attic? Mike was in the attic!

'Aah. The attic!' Noguchi exclaimed, and Ludi followed him up the narrow stairs. They crouched together in the empty musty space.

'What made you come up here?' Noguchi asked.

'I supposed you wished to lift the tatami up here.'

'But there is no matting here.'

'I supposed that there would be.'

'We now know that there is not.'

Ludi followed him down the stairs. Suzuki was at the door, and Noguchi said to her, 'Do you suppose I may have a cup of water?' He accepted thankfully the cup she brought to him. He had wasted time. When he had shouted at this old country-woman he had not been himself, and the uneasiness in his heart was nothing to do with these people, nothing to do with the case. His hands fumbled as he put on the shoes that he had roughly kicked off on his entry. 'I shall see you tomorrow,' he said to Ludi, and he passed Mary wordlessly as she stood in the garden.

Mr Noguchi was feeling ill. Dire premonition hastened his foot-steps. He had heard of weird things happening to other people, but to him – never! And now he had heard his wife's voice call to him, and he was terrified. 'Anata, you . . .' she had called; he had *heard* her!

Japanese husbands and wives seldom use the given name when addressing each other. Anata – you, they say. It can be spoken in many ways, with anger, with love, or teasingly. His wife's voice had come to his ears as he had never before heard it, urgently, pleadingly. 'She's dead!' said Mr Noguchi, forlornly. He spoke aloud – with certainty.

That evening, when his daughter, distraught and travel-stained, came to seek him at the inn, he did not need to hear her frantic tale. 'Father, she was burnt . . . she is dead. . . .'

Placing his hand gently over his daughter's mouth, he said, 'Enough! We shall talk, and weep, later. Now, you shall sleep.'

Taking one of the tablets sent to him by Doctor Kimura, he insisted that she swallow it, and he sat beside the sleeping girl. Twice, through the night, he heard the mountain-muffled sounds of far-off bombings.

'Enough! Too much! More than enough . . .' he whispered.

22

LUDI was hauling the sleep-mats from the cupboard, as though sure that he would find Mike hidden among them. Suzuki stood watching, a proud expression on her face. 'Not there!' she cried.

'Mike, poor Mike!' cried Mary hysterically, as she ran into the house from the garden.

'Where is he?' roared Ludi. 'Where the devil is he?'

Suzuki rushed out to the well. He heard the geek geek of the rusty windlass handle as she let the pail down.

Mary went to the door of the latrine, a primitive deep hole, in a little annexe to the cottage at the rear. Opening the door, she pointed. 'He's down there!'

Peering into the dark depths, Ludi saw that indeed Mike was – down there. Lying flat, he put his strong arm into the cesspool.

'Mike!' A hand met his, he heaved strongly.

'What a stink!' gasped Mike.

'Exactly,' answered Ludi. 'Let's move,' and he wondered at the things a man would do to save himself.

Mike's clean-up was accomplished; all Doctor Kimura's soap used up. Suzuki set alight a lump of raw sulphur, for she was determined to have an odourless house.

Ludi called to her: 'You'll choke us to death. Come here.'

'Hai hai – yes?'

'Tell us what makes you so wonderful? Sit down, and tell us.'

'Me! Wonderful? No, no, no.'

'Yes, you.' Ludi spoke adoringly. 'Isn't she the smartest...'

'The most,' said Mike.

'So clever,' praised Mary.

'Let her talk,' ordered Ludi. 'Let her tell us.'

This was a great moment for Suzuki. Her entire life had been spent in service. This moment, with three people sitting gazing at her in admiration and affection, was the peak of her career. She intended to enjoy it.

Lighting her tiny brass-bowled pipe, she took a dainty puff and, speaking in English so that Mike would be amazed at her fluency, she began, 'Ludi Sama, when you went outside house, my mind was up and down and round and round.' She made these movements with the hand holding her pipe. 'Nowhere, but nowhere to hide Mike San. Then – I knew! Toileto only place! No Japanese, even clever one, never look there.'

'How did you think of it?' asked Ludi.

'I – don't – know,' answered Suzuki in a voice full of wonder.

'And how were you so certain that no Japanese would ever look for me there?' asked Mike.

Suzuki, sitting very straight, looked everywhere but at her audience. 'Too dirty,' she said. 'No Japanese can even think a man could go in there.'

'And I did,' complained Mike.

'So! Yes, I know,' said Suzuki, in an embarrassed voice.

Ludi smiled to himself, for he had caught a tiny gleam of triumph in those old eyes. Was this Suzuki San's way of striking a blow against the Yanks? He grinned – yes, no doubt about it. Well, good luck to her.

Late that night, Ludi spoke seriously. 'Mike must leave here. We must never again run the risk we did today.'

'Where can I go?'

'I'll go down to the village, talk to some people I know there, sound them out, see if they'll help.'

'It's too risky,' cried Mary. 'Trust nobody.'

'Then may we have your suggestion?' asked Ludi politely.

'Yes, you may,' Mary answered with spirit.

'Well?' Ludi waited, a half-smile on his lips.

'Well . . .' she hesitated. 'There must be some other way. . . .'

'Tell us, please do,' Ludi spoke flatteringly. 'Don't be modest, Mary. I'm sure you have a wonderful plan. Your ideas are so unusual, so practical.'

'Wrap it up, Ludi,' said Mike unhappily.

'Your slang talk goes over my head,' Ludi objected.

'Just stop knocking Mary!' Mike smiled at her. 'Ludi, I don't want to leave here – that is, I mean, unless it is too dangerous for you all.'

'We love having you,' gushed Ludi. Without warning, a feeling of anger and frustration was upon him. He *would* take up his rucksack, walk out into the night. No, he knew he couldn't do that, and he waited a moment before saying quietly, 'Mike, it's time we told you the facts of the case!' He told him what had happened to Captain Tanaka. 'So, you see, we are not only guilty of sheltering an enemy, we – Mary and I – are a pair of cold-blooded murderers.'

'Not cold blood,' breathed Mary.

'Hot blood, then, if you prefer it that way. . . .'

Mike interrupted. 'Was Noguchi looking for the body of the policeman here, today?'

'He was not sure what he was looking for, but it was, in fact, for you! He was looking for the "why" we killed Tanaka.'

'Me? My God!'

'That's right! My God also.' Ludi crossed himself.

Mike looked at him curiously. 'Are you religious?'

'I'm many things, some of them unsavoury, and, unless we arrange things more cleverly, I am going to be an inmate of a Japanese prison. So are we all. Now I, personally, would not like that.' He waited.

'I do want to stay here,' said Mike, 'if it's possible.'

Ludi turned to Mary; she met his gaze defiantly. 'Mike should stay here!'

Suzuki had not been able to grasp the entire conversation. Ludi told her carefully and asked, 'What do you think, old lady?'

'Anywhere is no good!' Suzuki announced.

'She's right. Nowhere is no good.' Ludi stood up, and said wearily, 'O.K., Snooks, you stay here.'

'Don't call him that,' protested Mary.

'Sounds fine to me,' said Mike, then suddenly he gasped, in acute pain, 'my arm that was cut off, it's hurting like hell!'

'He gone crazy?' Suzuki looked worried.

'No,' said Ludi. 'He's not crazy.' He put his arms around Mike, held the younger man against him. 'Come on, Mike, it's all right, it's all right now.'

Almost immediately Mike quietened down. Watching them, Mary remembered the time when she had been soothed, in the same manner, against the same shoulder. She listened as Ludi said, 'Mike, you are feeling phantom-pain; it happens to practically everyone who loses a limb. You'll learn to deal with it. You will, you know. You feeling better now? Of course you are.'

'I guess so, and I'm terribly tired. I am terribly tired,' he repeated apologetically.

'Me, too. I'm turning in.' Ludi looked at Mary. 'You take first watch,' he ordered.

'Why me? What is wrong with you?'

'I need a good long sleep,' he said callously.

'And I don't?'

'And you don't. But I'll walk with you part of the way.'

'Whatever for?'

Receiving no answer, she followed him outside. In the darkness he drew her to him; Mary moved abruptly away, but he caught and held her closely.

'Ludi?' Mike called from the doorway.

Tearing herself away from Ludi's encircling arms, she whispered accusingly, 'You knew that he would be watching. You want Mike to think that I am your girl.'

'Coming soon, Mike,' said Ludi calmly. 'Go on, Mary!'

'You want to spoil things between Mike and me.'

'There could never be anything to spoil.'

'There is – there could be – will be.'

'Poor Mike!' said Ludi dolorously. She raised her hand in a fury; he caught and held it. 'Were you going to hit me?' he laughed.

'Yes. If only you knew . . .'

'Knew what?'

'That I hate you!'

'Come now, not hate – surely not hate? Why, just ten seconds ago you were on – er, – fire for me and . . .'

'Shut up!'

'I hear, and shall obey.' Ludi spoke lightly. 'Deus abencoa, Minha Senhora.'

'What does that mean?' she asked suspiciously.

He was silent for a moment. 'I don't really know why I said it. It means "God be with you, Lady!" It's Portuguese.'

'Oh,' she said, blankly.

'I take it back,' said Ludi, rudely.

'No, no please don't, I'm superstitious!'

'I take it back, and hope that the Japanese ghost lady with the egg face haunts you at the rock tonight; I hope that fiery ghost-balls will fly through the air and singe your hair. Gooda-nighto, Mary Sama. You don't know what's good for you – poor misguided girl. Now go on watch!'

He chuckled wickedly, and went into the house.

23

NOGUCHI was awakened early by the innkeeper.

'A policeman from the next village, he wishes to speak with you.'

'I will see him at once.'

The man proudly told his story. 'Two farmers were clearing water hyacinths from a pond on their land. A farmer and his old wife, to be exact – very good people . . .'

'Yes, yes. Get on with the facts.' Noguchi sensed what was coming; he was impatient.

Refusing to be hurried in reporting the biggest event of his career, the village policeman continued, 'The old woman felt something unusual beneath her feet whilst wading in the dark water. Hitching her kimono higher about her legs, pushing sleeves as high as her shoulder, she plunged an arm deep down. Her hand grasped another hand. Aaarah, Maa! The horror of the thing! A

dead man! And more than shocking, a murdered man, dressed—'
Fingering the serge cloth of his uniform, and leaning over until
his face was but an inch from the face of Noguchi, he whispered,
'A policeman's uniform! And, what is more – ' he saluted proudly
– 'I am here to announce that I have discovered the body of
Captain Tanaka!' He waited, chest expanded with pride.

Noguchi said nothing, until the air in the man's chest had
been expelled. 'Wait outside for me. Keep your lips together,' he
ordered.

Re-entering the room where Yuriko lay sleeping, he gazed
down at her face, and was appalled by its sharp, pinched look.

He would have to go at once to the place where Tanaka's body
had been found, and make full inquiries there – for how long?
No rations had been handed out here for many days; he had tried
to obtain food last night, done his best, to no avail. Ah, she was
awake, sitting up, adjusting the fold of her sleeping-robe. How
beautiful young women were when they awoke from sleep. No
rough beard. He must obtain food for this one before he went off
to his job. But where? How?

'Good morning Yuri-chan,' he replied to her greeting. That pet
name, so long since he had used it!

My father is an old man, she was thinking. How tired, how old
he looks today. 'What? No smile for your child?' she teased.

'There should be one somewhere, I know I have one somewhere.'
He searched diligently. 'I knew it! There! How's this?' Placing a
closed fist against his lips for an instant, he took it away, and smiled.

This game from baby days delighted her; she smiled back at
him trustingly. Noguchi knew now that he would have to do as he
had intended to do all along, distasteful though it would be.
Ordering the deflated village policeman to await his pleasure,
he started on the rough track up the mountainside. At the top, in
the small house there, he would ask Hoffer for food.

Ask for the food first. Arrest Hoffer first? If I arrest him first,
impossible to ask for food. If I ask such an immense favour, how
shocking then to . . . *I shall ask for the food!*

No one was at the turn in the track, but someone had been

there not long before. What a rich supply of tobacco, three more newly-smoked butts.

He walked slowly on towards the house, Aah, Hoffer! There he was at the well. How healthy, how glowing he looked.

Ludi spoke pleasantly. 'Ohio de Gozimasu, Noguchi Sama.' Perfect inflexion, perfect Japanese. My English is also excellent. Childish perhaps, but he would reply in English.

'Good morning to you, Mr Hoffer.' Now, for the embarrassing request. But Hoffer again spoke first. 'Found Tanaka yet?'

Outrageous, confound the man! 'Yes, Mr Hoffer. We have found his murdered body.'

'So you were right?' said Ludi, as though in amazement.

'Yes, I was right! We both knew that, didn't we, Mr Hoffer?'

'Speak for yourself, Mr Noguchi.' Ludi towelled his face briskly. 'I am sticking to my story. Do you want me to come along with you now?'

'If you please.'

'Right! I'll tell Mrs Ogata. Shall I be away long?'

'I do not think you will be coming back at all, Mr Hoffer.'

'Mary,' yelled Ludi.

Her startled face appeared at the tattered paper window. 'What is it, Ludi?'

'Noguchi San has found Tanaka.'

No sooner had the words left his lips than he regretted them, but her reaction was not as he had feared. 'Thank God!' she said quietly, and came into the garden wearing a cotton kimono. It was very short, coming only to the smooth calves of her legs.

'Good morning, Mr Noguchi.' She adjusted the neck of her robe, and he almost expected to hear this girl also say, 'What, no smile for me?' To prevent such a ridiculous occurrence, he smiled quickly, 'Good morning, Mrs Ogata.'

'Is the Captain alive? Where was he? I am glad . . .'

'He is dead,' said Ludi flatly.

'No!'

'Yes,' answered the men simultaneously

'Dead,' sighed Mary.

'Worse,' said Ludi outrageously. 'Murdered.'

'Murdered?' Mary's hand went to her throat.

'O.K., Mary.' Ludi spoke harshly. 'Stop the drama; you always hated him. You'd better get dressed.' He turned to Noguchi. 'Do you want her to come with us?'

'I think not.'

'Just me?'

'Just you, Mr Hoffer.'

'Where shall we be going?'

'I do not quite know; I am not well acquainted with this district; you know it better than I.'

'So I do.' Ludi's mind began to seethe. Trapped. Caught by little people, little circumstances. Mike, Mary, Suzuki San – why should he sacrifice his future for them? They would all go their separate ways when the war was over, and would they think of him? Noguchi was arresting him also because he had his mother's dossier from Shanghai. A curse on all prostitutes that gave birth to sons. You couldn't climb out of muck; you could try, but someone always knew you.

Focusing back to reality, Ludi was astounded to hear Noguchi saying, in a voice of desperation, 'Mr Hoffer, will you sell me some food?'

What was the old fox driving at now? 'Did you say food?' Ludi looked down at Noguchi in genuine perplexity.

'Food. I have no food to give my child, my daughter, who arrived yesterday to stay in this village. Her mother, my wife, was killed a few days ago, in Tokyo.' Noguchi bowed apologetically. 'Will you sell me something?'

'No.'

'Ah! So!' Noguchi bowed once more. Tears came welling from his eyes, rolling down his cheeks for the foreign man and woman to see. Shame, shame and weakness! What had become of the once proud world? Where was common sense and decency? In his own country, he stood on top of a mountain and begged food from a man he was about to arrest for murder. His wife dead, gone, burnt up . . .

99

Walking to the well, he dipped his handkerchief into the clear cool water in the pail, soaked it, and raised it to his eyes.

Ludi went into the house. Mary remained with Noguchi in the garden. The sun now filled the air with warmth; from the towering volcano spirals of ghostly white-grey smoke issued, seeming to spell out a message – warning. Something dreadful was about to happen. To Japan? To the world? 'Mrs Ogata,' said Noguchi, faintly, 'do you have the feeling of something about to happen, a foreboding?'

'I feel nothing,' Mary answered. 'Excuse me, I should go into the house, to say good-bye to Mr Hoffer.'

'Certainly,' said Noguchi. 'I shall wait here for him.'

'What to do now, Ludi Sama?' Suzuki was asking, as she tied up the ends of the purple furoshiki parcel.

'What is in the furoshiki?' asked Mary.

'Food,' Suzuki stated bluntly.

Ludi took the bundle. 'There is nothing anyone can do now. We've slipped up – badly.'

'You will sink of somesing.' Suzuki spoke with strong confidence. She went to the window, keeping watch on Noguchi.

'It's obvious to me what you will think of,' Mary said scornfully to Ludi. 'You are going to clear out, desert us.'

'Go back outside,' ordered Ludi. 'Do you want Noguchi to come into the house?'

Mary glanced out through the window. Noguchi was standing in deep thought at the well. 'He's not even thinking of us,' she said, and, turning to Ludi, she put her hand on his arm. 'You can't run away! I know you are intending to, I know . . .'

Ludi brushed her hand away. 'That "no touch" clause of yours works both ways,' he said quietly. 'I am running nowhere.'

'Then why are you taking the food?'

'It is for Noguchi's child!' Picking up the bright cloth bundle he turned to Suzuki. 'I don't know what will happen; I may be taken to Tokyo. Old Lady, you should leave here, you can do no good here any more.'

Suzuki smiled crookedly. 'Like you, I will do somesing.'

Ludi put his hand on the frail old shoulder and, passing Mary as if she were a chair, he walked to the bedding cupboard. 'Mike!' he whispered.

'Yes?' came a muffled voice.

'Noguchi is arresting me. Try and hold on a while, the end of the war can't be far off.' Walking swiftly out of the house, he joined Noguchi.

The two men walked to the village in silence. Arriving at the Inn, Noguchi spoke. 'I will ask you to step inside with me; I wish to see my child.' He had regained his composure.

'Of course, your child! Mr Noguchi, I said that I would not sell you food, but—' He held out the bright bundle.

Noguchi hesitated. 'I am aware that no one can spare food,' he said stiffly.

'No one but me; I always have things to spare.'

'Indeed!' Noguchi longed to grab the food and rush to Yuriko, but the position was embarrassing to a degree. For the first time in life he was a beggar. Glancing at the face above him, he was startled by the sweetness of Ludi's smile.

'Mr Noguchi, I give you this food – with pleasure!'

The young man meant it. 'You are generous, I thank you.' Taking the parcel of food with hands that trembled slightly, he walked along the dark corridor that led to his daughter's room.

After a few paces he halted, turned, and with a stiff little bow, said: 'As you are, for the time being, my prisoner, Mr Hoffer, I suppose that you will not mind waiting outside for a few minutes, until I return?'

'Certainly, Mr Noguchi.' Ludi spoke cynically. 'I'm in no hurry!'

24

ALONE at the Inn entrance, Ludi leaned against the wall. He did not have to wait long. A disturbed father, accompanied by the innkeeper, emerged. They were arguing angrily. 'Why did you let her go out?' Noguchi was demanding.

'I had no power to stop her.' The man's voice was surly.

'You know that she is weak – no food . . .'

The innkeeper looked the important man from Police Headquarters directly in the eyes. 'Frankly, Noguchi San, I have no interest in either you or your daughter. I have children of my own with empty bellies. I have troubles of my own.'

'I must find her, she is all I have,' muttered Noguchi, in deep distress.

'We will look for her now,' said Ludi.

'We?'

'Yes, she can't have gone far, and children are amazingly tough. When I was a child, I was often without food for days on end, and told to find food for myself when I complained.'

'You!' Noguchi brushed aside the tribulations of Ludi's childhood.

'Yes! I was a very nice little boy.'

'Perhaps so, Mr Hoffer. I am not myself today. Excuse me, you will have to excuse me.'

The old fellow was certainly not himself. 'Don't you think we had better start searching for her? You are wasting time.'

'Yes, I realise that.' Removing his spectacles, Noguchi wiped the lenses carefully on a piece of tissue. 'She is a stranger here; if she wandered far, she would be hopelessly lost.'

They went out together into the brilliant alpine sunshine. 'Describe your daughter to me – what age is she?' Ludi asked.

'Ignoring this question, Noguchi exclaimed, 'No need to search – there she is coming now!'

Down the road walked an extremely pretty Japanese girl, tall, and about eighteen years of age. Noguchi spoke sternly in English to her. 'Why did you leave the Inn? I have been worried!'

Yuriko giggled and put her hand over her mouth.

'What is amusing you?' asked her father.

She bowed, a smile of deep affection on her face. 'I smile because you speak to me in a foreign language,' she said in Japanese.

Noguchi also smiled slightly. 'No wonder! For you have disrupted my entire day, and as your English is excellent, I shall not repeat my questions.'

'Is this your child? I was under the impression that you were worried about a small girl!' exclaimed Ludi.

'No matter what age, a daughter is always a child to her father.' Noguchi was obviously himself again. Drawing Yuriko aside, he explained about the food – enough for a few days; she would find it in the purple furoshiki, in her bedroom.

She kept nodding her head, looking over her father's shoulder. Was Ludi receiving some of the little nods? Could he be mistaken? Was there not an ingredient in the nods coming his way that were not intended for the father?

He was not mistaken – the little imp! He winked at her.

The apricot cheeks flushed. Noguchi seemed not to have noticed his daughter's behaviour. 'Mr Hoffer, my daughter wishes to thank you for your kindness.'

'Domo arigato.' Straight black lashes veiled her eyes.

Noguchi continued, 'Mr Hoffer, you and I shall travel by motor-car to the next village; we may be there some time, a few days, perhaps. Have I your permission, if we are detained longer than I hope, to allow my daughter to ask Mrs Ogata for food? Could you give her a note to take to Mrs Ogata? An imposition, but . . .' his voice was tinged with embarrassment.

Ludi almost felt pity for him, but enough was enough! This girl could cause disaster to the people at the little house. 'Surely you, in your important official position, can find another way! Mrs Ogata has much less chance than your daughter of getting anything to eat. I am sorry.'

'Ah.' Noguchi spoke stiffly. 'Forgive me. I shall not worry you much longer with my personal affairs.'

Why did so many Japanese people take refusal as a personal insult? *'I'm in no hurry,'* said Ludi.

'Perhaps not, but I am.' Noguchi defiantly gave detailed instructions to his daughter, describing the way up to the house.

Well! Mary would have to deal with her! Time was flying by; Tanaka would be an unpleasant object to behold when they reached the place where his body had been found. Ludi couldn't care less; he would have an answer to everything; play for time, drag things out. When the war was over, the Japanese would be in a very bad position; he had heard from short-wave radio about war crime trials, a new expression to the world. There were rumours in the village that Germany, already defeated, was to have such trials. Well, there would be many Japanese eating humble pie soon.

Noguchi was ushering his daughter into the Inn, giving her no chance to look at Ludi again. So, Father had noticed the looks and nods? Of course he had; the old man was – what was that expression Mike used so often? – 'on the ball.'

'Well, so am I,' murmured Ludi, to himself.

Again Noguchi emerged, walking briskly. 'Now,' he said, 'you will come with me, Mr Hoffer, to the place where you attempted to hide Captain Tanaka's dead body.'

'Not admitted,' said Ludi, calmly. 'But of course I shall go with you. Not much choice, have I?'

25

MR NOGUCHI felt as though he had been wrung out, like a sheet after a brawny housewife had tortured and twisted every drop of water from it. He decided that he would take two men with him, in addition to the local policeman who had reported the finding of the body. The junior police in the station were obtuse types, but they were Judo experts. He glanced sideways at Ludi. What had the man done to cause Yuriko to blush so deeply? His innocent flower-like daughter. . . . This man was not to be trusted, in any way.

Outside the police station an ancient American motor-car with a charcoal-gas attachment, stood waiting. The younger policeman was putting more charcoal into the grotesque burner. The car, beginning to choke and sputter, started on its journey; Noguchi and Ludi sat together in the back seat, absorbed in their individual thoughts.

The village to which they went was small, and as they drove along its main street, news spread that the murderer of the Police Captain was arriving. A small crowd gathered. 'We are going to have an audience,' said Ludi.

'It seems so,' Noguchi agreed.

'I'd like to know what you expect to gain from bringing me here?'

'I have brought you here to see if any of the people recognise you.'

'I know this village like the back of my hand! I know everyone in it.'

'You admit that?'

'Admit it! Mr Noguchi, the farmers here are my partners in crime.'

'In what crime?'

'They will be scared out of their wits when they see whom you have brought along to be identified. They'll think that it's a dirty police trick to inquire into their selling of food on the black market!' Ludi laughed heartily.

Noguchi spoke angrily. 'Your insulting opinion of the Japanese intellect and morals will cause you sorrow one day. Perhaps today.'

'Ah! Soo!' mocked Ludi and hopped briskly from the car.

Noguchi was enraged to see him winking, making hush-hush signs to the dozen or so elderly farmers gathered about them. 'Mr Hoffer, stop being so ridiculous!'

The expressions on the faces about them were enough to make Hoffer's predictions seem correct. The man had a way of having luck on his side; but this was murder – and Hoffer had killed Tanaka. Why? Why? That question had become an obsession in Noguchi's mind.

Not one person in the village admitted to having seen Ludi Hoffer before. The old farmer in whose pond Tanaka's body had been found lost all sense of importance, and actually showed the whites of his eyes when questioned. Both he and his wife changed visibly, unashamedly, from being the stars of the drama, into a modest old couple, whose only desires were to be allowed to return home and forget ever having been so important.

Noguchi was disgusted with his people. Not one had courage; not one stood out and spoke the truth. To make matters worse, Hoffer continued to smirk and make little signs of recognition which were studiously ignored by the villagers.

Keeping his dignity, Noguchi climbed back into the snorting car, whose engine had been wheezily chugging on during their visit. 'It is not necessary to view the body.' He spoke tersely to the local officials, and gave them instructions. Then he turned to Ludi. 'Be seated again in the car,' he said. 'We shall return immediately to the big village, for further investigation of the motive for this crime.'

'Well?' said Ludi smugly, after a mile of road had slipped by. 'I told you how it would be. Now, it is up to you to raise up Japanese morals and intellect in my opinion.' He laughed. 'I think they were all just as smart as can be.'

'Smart?' Noguchi mouthed the word in disgust. 'Yes, you would think lies and evasion, smart. Such characteristics have made up your life.' He relapsed into stern silence.

Hoffer would not be so light-hearted when he found that, instead of returning to the house of Mrs Ogata, he would be locked up in a cell at the police station while this matter was sifted to the dregs, to find the missing piece of the puzzle – the *motive*.

106

26

THEY re-entered the village of foreigners that the Americans would never bomb.

As they chugged along the machi, the driver exclaimed, 'What goes on?' The main street, always so deserted, where even children usually walked quietly, was now a seething mass of noisy excited people. Germans, Italians, French, Russians, citizens of neutral nations or nations allied to Japan, and local Japanese residents, men, women, and children, were all in the excited throng. Ludi saw a German acquaintance, and called out to him, 'What has happened?'

The noise of many voices made it impossible to hear even shouted words. Shrugging his shoulders expressively, thumb of his right hand pointing up, left thumb pointing down, the German pulled a face and shook his head.

Ludi turned to Noguchi. 'Make the driver stop!' A wild hope had been born in his heart. Was this the end of the war? The lousy stinking war. That hope died as quickly as it had been born, for the faces in the crowd wore expressions of bewilderment, stupefaction – yes, and fear.

Noguchi spoke to the driver. 'Stop – this instant!'

The driver desired nothing more than to stop and satisfy his own curiosity, but he was tired of being hungry, and of kow-towing to superiors. 'I have too much initiative to stop here in the middle of the road,' he replied boldly. A thrill tingled the length of his spine, for he received no reprimand. He added to the din about them, pressing heavily on the horn, and then brought the old car to a stop.

Noguchi poked his head out and questioned a well-dressed Japanese man. 'Can you tell us the reason for all this excitement?'

'Haven't you heard the news?'

Must they go through the agony of Japanese conversational ball-tossing? Ludi interrupted, 'Just tell us. What is happening?'

He received an impassive look from the man, who awaited Noguchi's reply to his question.

His countryman obliged. 'No. I have heard nothing. I am deeply puzzled.'

'Soo! Everyone is most puzzled – and shocked.'

'So it appears. Do you know the reason?'

'The reason? Soo! Yes, I heard on the radio.'

'Aah! The radio, on the radio. Will you kindly relay to me the news you have heard?'

'Certainly.'

'Thank you.'

'The radio news said that this morning the city of Hiroshima was completely destroyed, and that practically all the people of that city are dead.'

Hiroshima! Ludi felt deflated. Probably an earthquake.

'How destroyed? How could a city be so quickly destroyed?' Noguchi asked, in an agitated voice.

'They say – the radio announced . . .' the man's voice became very solemn. 'They say that a bomb, just *one* bomb was dropped on it.'

Noguchi grabbed at the arm of the stranger. 'One bomb! Only one bomb? What kind of bomb?'

'It was just said a bomb – no name was given it.' The man resented Noguchi's grip on his sleeve. 'Kindly let go of me.'

'I am sorry, excuse me. Did the news mention anything else?'

'It said that the light, the flash, given out by the bomb was like no other seen on this earth. Those who saw it, even from afar off, were blinded by it.' Pulling his arm free of Noguchi's grip, he disappeared into the crowd.

Before the men in the car had time to digest this startling news, there was a swirling movement in the crowd, and a hush fell over the people as they stood back to allow a group of soldiers to march through. Bayonets gleamed and there was a smart tempo to their marching. It seemed that they were to do a little work, to restore order.

Noguchi, it appeared, was strongly against these tactics.

Leaping from the car with surprising agility, he shouted to the lieutenant: 'No, no, these people are under civil law; there is no need for force.'

'They are out of hand,' shouted the lieutenant.

Noguchi removed his glasses and peered at the soldiers surrounding him. 'I am in charge of civic duties; these foreign people are under my jurisdiction; you will leave things to me.'

'What do you intend to do?' asked the lieutenant.

'Exactly nothing.' Replacing his glasses, Noguchi continued, 'It is natural for them to gather together at this time. They are in more dread than we, for we are in our own land, but they must fear us as well as this new threat that appears to be now upon us all.'

The young officer appeared undecided. Noguchi changed his tactics. Speaking flatteringly, he continued, 'Such people as these will cause no trouble, I assure you, not whilst you are here. They will disperse quietly, I assure you.'

He was a clever old cuss. Ludi watched the lieutenant pull in his chin and glare at the crowd, who were, in fact, beginning to thin out.

Noguchi then beckoned to Ludi, who followed him into the police station. Taking a small brandy flask from his pocket, Ludi offered it to Noguchi with a half-smile. 'Have a drink, to round off the day?'

'Thank you, no, I am sorry, but our day is not yet rounded off, Mr Hoffer.'

'Mr Noguchi, I am tired and completely fed up; so can't we call it a day?'

'I also am, as you so aptly put it – fed up. No, Mr Hoffer, we cannot call it a day. I have decided to have you locked up, for a time, at least. I shall, in the meantime, go about my business. This news of Hiroshima may change my plans.'

To be locked up at any time would have been a heavy ordeal, but for it to happen now, when things were, as Mike would say, cooking, was the limit! Ludi felt in his pocket for cigarettes. Four packs! He would ration them.

Entering the small cell, he decided not to think of it as a prison but just as a room, and catch up on his sleep. Stretching out on the narrow bench, he closed his eyes. Faint sounds came from the street, but soon even these ceased, and he slept soundly.

The sun went down, the people returned to their homes, but few adults slept that night. Hopes that the new and dreadful bomb might mean that the end of the war was in sight filled their tired minds. Then there was the added fear of Japan with her back to the wall, and this was not a comforting thought.

Those with access to secret short-wave radio sets crept through the village, going from villa to villa, spreading news that the Hiroshima bomb was – atomic!

'Atomic!' To the men it was a matter for scientific wonder and speculation, beyond the grasp of their war-tired minds.

To the women, it meant perhaps, one way or the other, the end of the war – but not yet – and next day, the children continued to play and to complain of hunger.

No sooner had Ludi Hoffer been locked in his cell than the telephone on Noguchi's desk shrilled. Headquarters ordered him to leave on the evening express for Tokyo. A hurried farewell to Yuriko, and he was on the train. Three times bombing-raids caused hold-ups. Noguchi was too weary to join the scurrying passengers, who, at each raid, jumped from the stationary train to lie flat on the ground, as they now knew only too well how to do.

While the bombs were falling, he thought of the last letter that he had received from his wife. 'Soon it will be autumn,' she had written. 'Do you recall how, year after year, we sat together in the garden with our friends, on the night of harvest festival. The sakē we drank, the sound of laughter? When shall we do this again?'

Never again!

'What shall I do?' he asked aloud in the emptiness of the train, while in the distance the crump! crump! of bombs shook the earth with hammer-blows of finality. But could it be true, he wondered, that *one* bomb, only one, had entirely destroyed the city of Hiroshima? If so, how dreadful, how terrible. Too much!

27

THE three people in the hilltop house, isolated, had heard nothing of the Hiroshima horror.

These days were, to Mary, almost happy. As she sat exchanging ideas, opinions, looks filled with understanding and, at times, an uncertain sweetness, it seemed to her that, for the first time in her life, she had found a person with whom she felt completely at ease.

Suzuki was on the outer edge of this pleasant contact. She sat for long hours alone at the rock, on the look-out, and fretted at Ludi's long absence, at their shortage of food, and at the acute danger they were in, of which Mary Sama now appeared to be oblivious. She was a foolish girl; needed pulling up.

'You gone a bit silly, a bit kichigai, Mary Sama?' Suzuki asked bluntly.

'Not at all,' said Mary indignantly. 'Why?'

'You are living in yumē – in a dream!'

'Well, it's a nice yumē, better than real.'

'Not nice, because yumē ends. Always people wake up, and then is truth.

A little disturbed at the coldness in the old woman's eyes and voice, Mary was too happy in her warm, friendly relationship with Mike to let it worry her deeply.

Suzuki continued to look reprovingly at Mary, who was not only seeing a mirage, but living in its very centre.

On the sixth day of Ludi's absence, Mary, taking a turn at the look-out, stared in unbelief at a Japanese girl walking up the track towards her.

The two young women took measure of one another, and Mary's heart beat unpleasantly fast.

To Yuriko the first view of this startled blue-eyed foreigner standing on guard against her further climb up the track was a challenge.

'Excuse me, this road leads only to my house,' said Mary.

Yuriko burst into delighted laughter. 'Your Japanese speech is amusing; you talk with a country dialect.'

'At least, you can understand me,' said Mary, frigidly.

In precise English, Yuriko replied: 'Oh, yes, I understand you, and it is to that house of yours I am going.'

'Why do you want to go to my house?'

'I am to see a man in that house.'

'There is no man, only my servant and I . . .'

'But I know of the man at the house!' Yuriko interrupted, and resolutely stepped past Mary to continue her climb.

'Just a moment!' Mary spoke furiously. 'It is my house; *only my servant and I live there!*'

'And the man,' sing-songed Yuriko, as, looking back laughingly, she scampered up the track, her rubber-soled shoes moving fleetly, scarcely seeming to touch the ground.

Mike, sitting in the sun, watched two girls running towards him, as if to a goal.

'What a fool you are!' gasped Mary. 'Why do you sit here? Just *sit* here – like this?'

The fair young man sitting so lazily in the sun, a young man with blue eyes, one arm, so different from the bold dark Hoffer San she had expected to see, dented Yuriko's aplomb considerably; but, tossing her head, she demanded attention. 'I knew there was a man,' she announced.

To Mike, the word 'man' on the lips of this kitten-faced girl sounded the most important word in the world. 'Who is she, Mary?' he asked hazily.

Yuriko gracefully unfurled a square of purple silk and waved it gaily.

Ludi's furoshiki! So that was it. 'Are you Mr Noguchi's daughter?' Mary's voice was dull. The mirage that she had been dwelling in vanished; and life as it was, full of danger, fear and uncertainty, came back to crush her.

'Yes, I am Yuriko Noguchi. I came to return this furoshiki to Hoffer San; he lent it to me.' Raising dark eyes to the blue skies above, she appeared to be thinking delicious thoughts about Hoffer San. Coming back to earth, with an innocent smile she spoke to Mike. 'He does not appear to be here. May I return it to you – Mr . . .?'

'Mike,' said Mike fatuously.

'Soo! Mike! Mike Sama. My father told me to come here; he said that you will give me food. I have no food and no ration ticket . . .'

Mike looked guiltily at Mary. 'Can we give her something?'

'Where is your father?' asked Mary stiffly.

'He is in Tokyo. I am afraid that he will be killed there, as was my mother.' Straight eyelashes lay closely against her cheeks. Mike watched, fascinated.

'How long has he been gone from the village? When will he return?' asked Mary.

The dark eyes flew open; Yuriko spoke coldly. 'That is my father's business.'

'Uh, huh! You should speak nicely to Mrs Ogata if you want her to help you,' teased Mike.

'I think that Mrs Ogata does not like me.'

'Of course she does. Mrs Ogata is good to everyone . . .' Mike's laugh trailed off abruptly.

'That's right,' said Mary bitterly. 'I am good to everyone. Stay here; I shall bring you something, and Mike San can tell you the story of his life while I am gone.'

'Mary, I was just sitting here and you both appeared so suddenly . . .'

The daughter of Noguchi! As Mary disappeared into the house, the seriousness of their position dawned in Mike's mind.

'Do *you* like Mrs Ogata?' Yuriko's unexpected question put him off balance. 'Is she a person you like much?'

Mike was about to say that indeed he did like Mary, but here perhaps, was the chance to do his bit, play his part in the intrigue. The Japanese girl showed her dislike of Mary. Could he trick this clear-eyed creature? 'I do not like her especially,' he lied.

'But she has food. You want food, so do I; so let you and I be partners. Will you join in a secret with me?'

'A secret – with you?'

'Yes, pretend that we like her, and keep it a secret from everyone that we come here, to get food.'

'You do not live here?'

'No, I come here only to visit.'

'Where do you live?'

'In the village.'

'From what country do you come?'

'I am a German.'

'You speak English like an American.'

'I have lived in America, but I am a German.'

'A very nice German.'

'And you,' said Mike with relief, 'are a very, very nice Japanese.'

'We, you and I, are both very, very nice,' Yuriko said solemnly.

'And we have a secret.'

'Two secrets,' stated Yuriko firmly. 'We will tell no one we come here to get our food, and we don't really like Mrs Ogata!'

'Of course,' agreed Mike traitorously.

'Shall we meet here tomorrow, Mike San?'

'On condition that you keep our secret from your father!'

'Do you know my father?'

'No, but I know that all fathers of beautiful girls don't like their daughters to have boy-friends – in Japan, that is.'

'That is so,' Yuriko smiled. 'Are you sure I am your friend?'

'Ssh! Yes, I am sure,' he whispered, as Mary and Suzuki San joined them.

Yuriko, turning to Mary, spoke modestly. 'You are kind, generous to me, but I was not polite to you; I am sorry.'

'That's O.K.'

'Thank you.' With a neat little bow, Yuriko accepted the refilled furoshiki. 'Where is his?'

'His?'

'My bundle of food,' Mike interjected. 'I must be going soon, so do you think you can give me my bundle now?'

'Yours is in kitchen!' Suzuki spoke in a sulky tone.

'I'll wait for you, Mike San.' Yuriko sat beside him.

'No, you had better go alone. We don't want anyone to see us together – do we?'

Her expression of disappointment faded. 'I will come tomorrow.' She smiled complacently.

In silence they watched Yuriko make her way down the track.

Mary was the first to speak. 'Well! Of all the fools!'

'Mike San not so fool,' said Suzuki.

'What could I do, Mary? It was all I could think of doing. She thinks I have a crush on her.' Mike swallowed a smile.

'Which, if I may be so bold as to say, you obviously have.'

'Don't be silly.'

'I'm not the silly one. Mike, you've done a terrible thing!'

'Not terrible,' stated Suzuki.

'I give up! That girl will ruin all that we have done to protect you. She is Noguchi's daughter – don't you realise?'

'She has promised me that she will not tell anyone she saw me here today,' said Mike desperately.

'Of course she will tell!'

'Won't tell, not yet, want to play love with Mike San.' Suzuki pursed her lips primly.

'For Pete's sake! Do you really think so?' Mike looked pleased.

'Her father probably sent her up here to spy on us!' said Mary, furiously.

'You were the one who allowed her to come up to the house, Mary!'

'How could I have stopped her? But, when she did come up, did you have to fall flat on your face to the brat?'

'Time to wake up now; dream, yumē, is all over. So, I always told you, Mary Sama,' Suzuki intoned deeply.

'Oh, shut up!' Mary hastily turned and went inside the house.

Mike and Suzuki looked at one another in embarrassment.

'Very rude – no need ever to be very rude. Shut up! is bloody rude word.' Suzuki was indignant.

'She's tired, Suzuki San. Tired of everything.'

'Mary Sama is shitsuren.'

'She's what? What does that mean? It sounds a very bad word!'

'*Is* bad word, meaning jealous.'

Glancing towards the house, then pointing to his chest, Mike asked: 'You mean . . .?'

'Soo! I mean, Mary Sama is jealous that you, maybe, like to play love with pretty Japanese girl.'

Joining Mary in the house, sitting beside her on the tatami, Mike took her hand, and asked, laughingly, 'Mary, are you jealous because you imagine that I want to play love with pretty Japanese girl?'

She looked at him in annoyance, and then, despite herself, smiled. He grinned back at her. 'A one-armed crock like me! Mary, you, as Suzuki says, are foolish garl. If I have any inclination to play love, with any girl in Japan,' he hesitated a moment, 'I assure you it is not with that Japanese brat. Isn't that what you called the poor little kid!'

'Mike! She is not a little kid. She is Noguchi's daughter. You must think of her only as that.'

'I'm wide awake to the danger. I told her that I'm a German, from the village; I guess I was as sharp as a tack to think of that one, now wasn't I? She's nothing to me – but you . . .'

'Yes?'

'You are the most wonderful girl in the world. All that you have done for me . . .'

The look in her eyes so full of questions! 'Ah, Mike, you are so nice!' she murmured.

Aghast at his cool thinking, at his resentment in being forced to speak words he didn't mean, Mike blurted out, 'Mary, when the war's over, will you marry me?'

The cloud of uncertainty in her eyes disappeared. Worth everything to have taken that look from Mary's eyes! Those scarred hands! He held one to his lips. 'Will you, Mary?'

She laughed happily. 'When this is all over, I'll marry you with pleasure, Mike!'

Suzuki trotted in from the garden. Jumping to his feet, Mike called, 'Suzuki San, Mary and I are going to be married when the war is over!'

Suzuki examined his face carefully. 'Why?' she asked stolidly. 'Why does anyone get married?'

'No use to ask me,' said Suzuki. 'I never did.'

'You should say you are happy for us,' declared Mary. 'Aren't you?'

'O.K. sure! I go to track and watch.' She gave a polite bow and left the room.

Suzuki squatted beside the rock; the sunshine was hot and she felt old, defeated. She had led a very empty life; no one had ever really cared for her; she had never been anyone's Number One. She rubbed her scarred leg gently; it was aching more than it usually did.

'Even if not true,' she murmured, 'it must be very good to have a man say he likes you.'

28

On her daily visits, Yuriko made it obvious that Mike was the only person at the house of any interest to her. Sometimes she and Mike talked outside, and sometimes she was invited inside, for a bowl of tea, or a bowl of gruel, which Suzuki prepared.

The old servant hovered around, as a guardian of the proprieties; but Mary, on pretext of going to the village, would go as far as the look-out rock, and wait for the girl to come down. Each day she waited longer than the one before.

She would hide in the bushes, and watch Yuriko go by. There could be no doubt that she was lovely, no doubt that the innocent affair with Mike was, to the girl, romance in its ideal form.

Once, passing Mary's hiding place, Yuriko stopped for a moment, and looking straight ahead, said: 'Good afternoon, Mrs

Ogata. Is it not very hot for you there in the bushes every day?'
Bending her head politely, she continued on her way.
In confusion, Mary remained sitting in the bushes. Indeed very hot! But not as hot as the indignity in her heart.

Her acute dislike of the Japanese girl astounded Mike, for as he insisted, he was playing a game, not only for his own benefit but for Mary and Suzuki as well.

'But Mike, it's a dangerous game! You should be able to see the subtle mind of that girl, the slyness behind her . . .'

'. . . kittenish ways,' finished Mike.

'She may have been a kitten when she was younger,' agreed Mary acidly.

One day, Yuriko, who had learned some German at the high school, proudly said to Mike: 'Wie geht es Ihnen, mein Freuud?'

Uncomprehending, Mike grinned. 'Now, stop talking in Japanese. You know I can't understand!'

'Oh!' said Yuriko, and was silent for a while, thinking deeply. Then she said solemnly: 'Mike San, don't you agree that Americans are wicked to drop the "A" bomb on Hiroshima?'

He smiled. 'Honey, your English is cute.'

'Cute? Why, Mike San?'

'You said, "the-a-bomb," but that's wrong! You can say, "*the* bomb," or you can say, "*a* bomb," but never "the-a-bomb!"'

'Soo!' Yuriko was silent again. 'I must go now, she announced suddenly.

'Are you offended with me for correcting your English?'

'Not at all, Mike San. But I did say correctly, "the A-bomb" as everybody says it.'

Without saying good-bye, she went down the track, and was soon out of sight.

'Now, what's cooking?' Mike mused, feeling strangely uneasy.

Mary, Suzuki and Mike had to face up to a menacing problem. 'No more food after tomorrow,' announced Suzuki.

'No rations at all in the village – are you sure of that?' Mike asked her.

'No rations. All stop many weeks ago.'

'But we can't just sit here and starve to death, doing nothing!' protested Mike.

'Can't we?' asked Mary cynically. 'Your girl friend has eaten the cupboard bare.'

'She *and* the rest of us,' said Mike.

'I go village, try to buy somesing,' announced Suzuki.

'It's no use, Suzuki San. You'll come back weaker than ever. Why bother?' Mary snapped.

'Better try than die – I try. Have you any Yen, Mary Sama?'

'Yes, but it's no use!'

Taking the money, Suzuki left the house. An hour later she returned, the money still clutched in her hand.

'I told you,' stated Mary. 'Ludi warned us.'

Suzuki lay on her bed. 'Not feeling good,' she announced, and turned her back to the room. 'Looks like no food anywhere; no one walking in village. No one talk to me. All close up; nowhere to find food anywhere.'

'She's right! There's nothing we can do.' Mary went to her own sleep-mat, and, pulling the cover over her, fell asleep almost immediately.

Mike moved to the window and looked out into the dusk. 'There must be some way to get food,' he said aloud.

He looked at Suzuki, for she was now watching him, eyes questioning, alert.

'What is it, Suzuki San?' he whispered.

Her eyes looked away from his. 'Mike San, on return from village, just a little way from here . . .'

'Yes, go on.'

'A house . . .'

'Yes?'

'On my way back from village, I saw old master of that house . . .'

She stopped speaking again. He said impatiently: 'Go on.'

Obviously not liking what she had to say, Suzuki pursed her lips as though a virtuous expression on her face could detract from the wickedness of her words, that now flew about the room like a flock of birds.

'Nice old Japanese master of that house, I saw today, being walked to village by two policemen. Policemen's faces proud like men when caught big fish. Old man's face angry, like small boy when father find him smoking tobacco. In that house, *first* house from here on way to village, not *near* village, but not so far away like *this*. In that house, was living, by himself, that old man, and I know, because of . . .' Suzuki pressed a hand against her heart 'because of feeling, here, that he go to prison and not come back to house.'

Mike had heard, from both Ludi and Mary, many things good and bad about Japan, and the Japanese way of life. 'It's a wonderful thing,' Ludi had said, 'that, even though the Japanese are desperate for lack of food, when a man plants a vegetable garden, in view and reach of all, I've never once heard of a case where the vegetables have been stolen. Don't you agree it's a fine thing?'

'Uh-huh! If what you tell me is true,' Mike had agreed.

'It's true,' Mary had assured him, in a voice that showed the Japanese up as a nation of nuts.

Mike now looked closely at Suzuki. Unhappy old girl, no doubt about that, but ready, willing and able to struggle on, and even to throw her deeply-ingrained moral values over the windmill.

She continued her story. 'I bet that poor old man got food left in that house.' She looked at him, and her eyes were desolate. 'O.K., Mike Sama?' she whispered.

'Certainly, O.K., why not?'

'Then – we go?'

'We go, together. Is it dark enough?'

'Dark enough – just right! Let's go.'

In the vacant house they discovered treasure indeed. The pungent peculiar odour of some articles Mike carried up the track caused him to doubt that they could be eaten. That stinking elongated, flaccid radish, eighteen inches long! Suzuki had so joyously pulled it from a wooden barrel of mush. 'Aara! Oshinko—*beautiful*! Delicious pickle,' she had whispered, gleefully. 'Put it back – it stinks!' Mike had said.

'Hah! You know but little,' and she had gone on collecting more of the outlandish objects in the kitchen. What Mike thought was a lump of wood, Suzuki hastily explained was *katsubushi* – dried fish, a nourishing food. After that, he'd made no more comments.

On their return, Mary awakened, and, like a sleepy-eyed child on Christmas morning, pulled Suzuki's large cloth bundle towards her and with trembling hands opened it, gloating over the contents. 'Condensed milk! Three cans! Seaweed, noodles, rice! I can't believe it! Unhusked, but we'll husk it!'

On seeing the stinking pickled radish, she seized it, rushed to the kitchen, slashed a piece off, washed it and came back to the room chewing it with relish.

'No accounting for tastes!' Mike grinned.

'I am ration boss,' declared Suzuki. 'Better you be ashamed, Mary Sama. This food we steal. No chance of ever getting anything more; plenty of chance of being in trouble for having it at all!'

'True,' admitted Mary, 'but I must have some condensed milk this very minute!'

The old woman went into the kitchen, and made two small holes in one of the milk-cans. She offered it to Mary, saying, 'Good that you have sweet thing. Make you sick maybe, but no matter.'

Suzuki lay sleepless and unhappy that night. She had aided and abetted murder. Treason, she supposed, she had committed. She had lied, and now she was a thief. There was nothing more bad to do.

29

Yuriko sat in the garden with Mike. 'Do you think my English is good, Mike San?' she asked.

'Your English is good, yes,' he answered vaguely.

'My knowledge of German is also a little good,' she stated proudly.

'You are a smart cookie.'

'Cookie? What does that mean?'

'There! You see! Your English is not so very good!' he teased.

'But better than the German of mein lieber Freund!'

His inertness gone, he asked: 'What do you mean?'

'Only that when I spoke to you yesterday, I spoke in German, and you told me "stop talking in Japanese." '

'I did?' Mike continued to gaze into the dark eyes so close to his own, and he had the uneasy feeling that he was about to be drawn in their depths – and then another feeling, that perhaps that would be a lovely death.

'Soo! Yes, you did!' Yuriko looked away from him, to the grey smoke wafting from the mouth of the volcano. Like a giant plume, it slowly fanned across the sky over the village. 'You are hiding in this place, aren't you? You never leave it.' She rose to her feet. 'I am a Japanese. We Japanese are taught that our country is of first importance – above life.'

'Is that so?'

'Yes.'

'Go on.'

'I said to you yesterday, "Mike San! Don't you agree that Americans are wicked to drop the 'A' bomb on Hiroshima?" Do you remember?'

'I remember.'

'You never heard of the "A" bomb?'

'It doesn't make sense.'

'Soo! Maybe to you, no sense. To me, it tells that you have never left this house. Never gone to the village since I first came here or ever, I think. I know, from many things you say, I know that you are an American and that you are hiding here.'

Surely there was no threat in this soft voice? 'Yuriko, does it matter what country a man belongs to?'

'In wartime it matters.'

'I suppose it does,' said Mike, slowly.

'Soo – I am a Japanese girl,' she said sadly, 'I am never again to come up here, never again to see you.'

'You are going to tell the police?'

'No – just never again come here. When a Japanese girl loves a man, she loves him even to her death. Does it make you happy to know that I would die for you?'

As though in a dream he watched Noguchi's daughter walk slowly from the garden and begin the rough descent to the village.

Going inside the house, Mike found Mary and Suzuki lying on their sleep-mats. 'Our visitor,' he told them, 'has gone, and she won't be coming back again. She knows that I am an American.'

'So your tactics have failed,' said Mary.

'On the contrary, they have succeeded,' said Mike, gloomily.

30

LUDI lay looking up at the wooden ceiling of the cell. He had just completed his daily push-ups, and soon the rotund little policeman would arrive with his bowl of rice gruel. These days had not been too hard to take. He had grown up in China, and some of the ancient philosophy of patience had maybe seeped into him.

For the first couple of weeks, it had been tough going. His cell, in the basement, was stuffy, dark and evil-smelling, and he had existed on the bowls of watery rice-gruel that Ohara San brought to him twice daily. Tasteless mush! Wisely, he'd eaten it slowly.

Yes, he had stood it pretty well, until his gaoler had discovered, and confiscated, his cigarettes. How he'd managed not to hit the cuss was a thing never to be understood. For four days he had suffered viciously, and then, for no apparent reason, Ohara had come one evening and yes, actually smiling, had requested him to 'Come this way, please.'

Things had greatly improved after that. His new cell was airy and clean; the food was the same, but he was now given five cigarettes a day.

Today, for the first time, sitting on the edge of his bunk, a feeling crept over him of anger and impatience. Slipshod footsteps approached, and the smooth round face of Ohara peered through the grille; the door opened. Ohara San stepped back. 'You are free to leave here now, Hoffer San.'

The man bowed with servility, and stood aside to allow him passage through the narrow door. 'You like to smoke, Hoffer San?' Ohara struck a match, held it to light Ludi's last cigarette. 'Hoffer San, I treated you very well when you in prison. You won't forget that – will you?'

Then Ludi knew. The war was over.

The Japanese stood uneasily before him. 'You won't forget, Hoffer San? The war is over – finished,' and he bowed his head.

Ludi ran a hand over the stubble on his face. 'You,' he ordered, 'bring me a razor, warm water – bring soap.'

As he shaved, Ludi looked closely at Ohara. What a modest, beaten, little man. 'When did the news come through?' he asked. 'Today?'

Ohara had the Japanese habit of putting his head to one side, then to the other, when unwilling to give out information.

'Today?' he repeated vaguely.

'You fool!' roared Ludi. 'Tell me when it ended!'

'Excuse me, Hoffer San, it ended many days ago, maybe even ten or fifteen. Don't blame me, please; I only obey orders. Orders today are that you may leave here – now.'

'Why not before? Why only today?'

'Because,' and now Ohara San looked ill, 'because news has come that conquering American troops are approaching this village. That's why, and, Hoffer San, remember I was good to you, and let me go now. American soldiers are nearing the village. My wife is young, and I fear for her.' He bowed deeply. 'Excuse me, please, Hoffer San,' he begged. 'May I go?'

Excuse him, please! Ludi raised a clenched fist, and then lowered it. The war was over. Why be bitter? He laughed. 'O.K. Ohara San. I won't forget that you were so good to me!'

Ludi walked into a world at peace. There were no soldiers with shining bayonets at the street corners, and few Japanese people walked abroad. The foreign residents who passed Ludi as he made his way along the machi called out cheerily to him: 'The Americans are coming!'

His first impulse was to walk on through the village, and up to that house hidden from sight among the trees on the hillslope. Then he realised that there would be nobody there. The war had ended days ago, and he supposed that they had already gone to Tokyo, taking Suzuki with them. The ideas that Ludi had had of using the rescue of Mike to his advantage with the American authorities, now seemed only absurd, embarrassing.

People came to speak to him. An old Russian musician, the young Canadian wife of a Japanese, two blonde Swiss girls. . . . With linked hands they swayed in a circle, laughing, calling that the Americans were coming at last. More people came running out of the houses to join them, and, with a rumbling of jeeps and trucks, the Americans arrived, to be quickly surrounded by excited, hungry people, laughing and crying.

An American Army captain spoke kindly, but with authority. 'Food will be handed out. Don't worry any more. Everything is O.K. We need interpreters who can speak English and Japanese well. Any volunteers for liaison officers please report to me, bringing your identification papers.'

Ludi volunteered. 'You'll do, I guess,' the captain said. 'But you'll have to go down to our Headquarters to be screened and appointed. You can go in one of our jeeps, leaving right away for Tokyo.'

Hustle! Bustle! Efficiency!

Peace. . . .

31

LIFE, since Ludi's release from prison, had passed with dizzying speed. It scarcely seemed possible that in three days he had been through, and seen so much.

Tokyo city! What a shambles. He had been bewildered by the bomb-damage. How pugnacious the Japanese had been to hold out so long. He admired them for it. It was what he would have done. He wouldn't give up something he loved – it would have to be taken from him in his death-throes.

Speaking both English and Japanese, he was in the thick of things, a valuable go-between, and already he had discovered how simple it was to smooth things out – for one side or the other. This could be done by interpreting in a not too genuine manner. Not ethical perhaps, but he didn't give a damn about that. If he had the chance to soften the interrogation of some unfortunate Japanese cuss being questioned about something for which he had obviously not been responsible, then Ludi would follow his own mind in the matter.

It gave him a good feeling in the streets or elsewhere when he encountered a group of Japanese who looked at him with stubborn and yet fear-filled eyes. They were looking not at *him*, but at the American uniform of a liaison officer; very nicely tailored too. His good feeling came at their relaxation when he spoke fluently, in a friendly manner, to them. They seemed amazed at friendliness from one who wore the uniform of a conqueror. Yes, that gave him a good feeling, and also warned him not to become overly proud; it would be so easy to become filled with self-importance.

He had asked for time off and had taken a quick trip to Yokohama, but the bank holding his money, like many official buildings, was closed for the time being.

Returning to the mountain village, in response to an urgent call for his services, he found that the former little police station was now United States Headquarters for that district.

The first man his eye fell on, as he walked in, was a weary but intensely dignified Mr Noguchi, standing among a group of local Japanese officials who were waiting to be interrogated.

'This,' the American officer announced, 'is Liaison Officer Hoffer, who will interpret for us.'

'How do you do, Mr Hoffer?' Noguchi smiled wryly.

'I'm fine. How is your daughter?' Ludi's eyes twinkled.

'You know this man?' asked the American officer.

Ludi rubbed a hand along his jaw. 'Yes, and a fine man he is.'

'From what we have seen and heard, there just aren't any fine Japs.'

Ludi looked directly into the eyes of the American. 'You'll be surprised,' he said, 'but there are some.'

Ludi had thought that he would have enjoyed helping to put the Japanese in their place. Some of them, yes; but, as the shocking tales of war atrocities were published, he remembered Suzuki, sitting on the tatami, sloshing her gashed legs with water already stained with the blood of Mike Peters.

This memory enabled him to carry out the job of liaison officer between the vanquished Japanese people and the victorious United States Army without prejudice.

Noguchi was questioned closely on his activities as police superintendent at the village during the last stages of the war. People in the village testified that he had been polite and reasonable. The authorities were convinced that Noguchi's slate was clean at the village, and he was ordered to return to Tokyo.

Ludi escorted him to the door.

'Mr Hoffer, please . . .'

'Yes, Mr Noguchi?'

'Would you do me the courtesy of telling me why you killed Captain Tanaka?' The detective took off his glasses and passed his hand across his eyes. 'My first failure to unravel a case. Ridiculous, perhaps, but I shall never rest until I know – why?'

He appeared so distressed that Ludi almost blurted out the reason for Tanaka's death. A flash of sanity overtook him. He could see the wily Noguchi having him arrested for the confessed murder of a Japanese policeman. 'Mr Noguchi, I didn't kill Tanaka.'

'Confidentially, I know you did; I *know* it. I only want to know *why*. What was it I failed to discover? It is making me quite ill.'

'I can only hope that you will feel better about it as time goes by. Good-bye, Mr Noguchi.'

'Good-bye, Mr Hoffer, and thank you.'

'For what? For giving you the biggest headache in your career?'

'No, not that! We, I suppose, shall never neet again. I am returning today to Tokyo city. No, Mr Hoffer, I do not wish to thank you for giving me a headache. I wish to thank you for your courtesy in several difficult situations!'

'Humph!' said Ludi, and he stood watching the defeated man walk slowly away.

The village was now crowded with American and other Allied Forces; three great sprawling hotels were reopened and used as Recreation Centres. It was as though the Americans had waved a wand, and presto! White-coated Japanese waiters, and gaily kimono'd, brightly lipsticked waitresses, food, whisky, cartons of cigarettes, a feeling of relaxed happiness, and hours of free talk.

Stories of the horrors committed by some units of the Japanese Army against prisoners of war streamed like a dirty flood about the ears of the village inhabitants.

War crime trials to come.

Tales of daring.

Tales of sorrow.

Tales of lucky escapes; some of these too tall to be believed.

Sitting in a rattan chair, dressed in his officer's uniform, glass in hand and slightly 'high,' Ludi listened as the talk flowed about him; the hotel-lounge was crowded; everyone wanted to talk, and to cap the story just told.

He listened vaguely to Captain Stephen Barnes talking to a brother officer, a young lieutenant. It was good to be among these men, to be accepted as one of them.

'I,' declared Barnes to his friend, 'think that your story stinks.'

'Stinks?' The young lieutenant was indignant.

'Yup!'

'It is a genuine true happening, I read it in a New York paper. Do you think those papers waste print on fables?'

A charming but rather childlike look of doubt appeared on Barnes's face. 'Well,' he began doubtfully, 'you say that you read it in a New York paper?'

'Yes, sir! That's where I read it. Do you believe it now?'

'Yes, maybe, but it's hard to believe that the police wouldn't find out.'

'Seems they didn't. This guy jumped from a bomber that was hit by flak, came down at night-time in a forest, somewhere in Germany, and . . .'

Ludi, half listening, didn't notice that the incident was in Germany; he nodded his head wisely.

'. . . Yes,' the lieutenant continued, 'that guy parachuted into the top of a tree, and was damn near killed. He fell out of the tree, and, next morning, a peasant found him . . .'

'A *peasant*?' Ludi interjected, indignantly.

'Sure, that's what it says in the paper. Well, it seems that this peasant didn't hand the airman over to the authorities. He took him and hid him, and got some doctor to attend to his injuries, and he kept that guy hidden, fed him and kept him there for a year until we marched in.'

'Seems incredible,' said Barnes. 'That peasant was sure taking a risk.'

'Well, it shows they're not all bad,' said the lieutenant. 'Great story, isn't it?' Ludi and Barnes, both mellow with alcohol, looked at him with approval.

Barnes turned to Ludi. 'What do you think of that? Some story, eh?'

'Yes, *sir*!' said Ludi hazily. He had found it easy to fall into American ways, especially in the matter of speech. 'Yes, siree!' he repeated more firmly, and leaned back in his chair to settle down to more drinking.

The talk flowed on around him. He floated happily, aware that he was slightly drunk, in this pool of normality in which he had at last come to harbour.

'Yes,' the lieutenant insisted. 'It's true. Wait a minute, I'll give you the name of the guy – it's on the tip of my tongue – hold on now. What the hell was his name?'

'Michael Peters,' said Ludi in a deep sure voice.

'No. Not Peters.' The lieutenant was annoyed. This was his story.

'My friend, Michael Peters.' Ludi opened his eyes and looked at the young man pugnaciously. 'That's who it was, man.'

'It was not!'

'Says who, it was not?' growled Ludi.

'I say it was not!' The men glared at each other.

'And may I ask who the hell you are?'

'You may not!' They rose unsteadily to their feet.

'Break it up,' said Barnes in no uncertain voice.

'Who the hell does this louse think he is?' demanded the lieutenant.

'It doesn't matter – just break it up.'

'Right! But I'm not going to sit here and be insulted.' The young man swayed off. Barnes and Ludi sat on in silence. Into Ludi's mind darts of uneasiness pricked uncomfortably, and suddenly hit him into full consciousness.

How was it that the village was not full of the wonder of Mike's miraculous escape? Why was it that the Americans, who apparently worshipped the spectacular, the unusual, had not carried Mike shoulder high through the village and taken him in triumph to Tokyo?'

Mike should by this time have been one of America's war heroes. 'It *was* Michael Peters, you know.' Ludi bent forward and tapped Barnes on the knee. Surely Barnes knew about Mike.

Barnes rose to his feet in boredom. 'I'm for bed, Hoffer. I never heard of your friend.'

'Never heard of him? Never heard of Mike Peters?' Ludi murmured, incredulously, as the captain, also swaying a little, walked along the corridor to his room.

What then had happened up there, in that little villa hidden among the trees near the hilltop?

Ludi rose unsteadily to his feet; he looked at his watch. It was 10 p.m.

Hurrying out of the hotel, he walked at a smart pace along the village street, his head clearing as he hastened.

32

COMING to the beginning of the rough track, Ludi broke into a run. On and up, he had never known the way to be so long. The house was in darkness, not a sound to be heard! He placed his hand on the door; it slid open easily, as Japanese doors do. Standing in the entrance, he listened intently. From habit he unlaced his shoes, and, slipping them off, stepped on to the worn tatami. Feeling the familiar springiness beneath him, he felt also, that he had come home.

'I'll sleep here tonight!' He spoke aloud, stepped forward, tripped and crashed to the floor.

Mary, for it was her sleeping body that he had fallen over, sat up and screamed; the room became crowded with clumsy movement.

131

Ludi, groping in the dark, put his hand on the swinging light-cord, and saw Mary, Mike and Suzuki huddling on their sleep-mats, looking at him, in dazed unbelief.

'What are you three damned fools doing up here?' he asked.

'What are *you* doing in that uniform?' Mike whispered.

'It came with the job.'

'The job?' Mike stared at him, with a sudden glimmer of comprehension; Suzuki and Mary remained in their huddled positions.

'Just a minute Mike – hold everything! Don't you know?'

'Know *what*?' Mike caught at him wildly.

'The war ended days ago! The village is crowded with United States troops, Japan is occupied by the Allied Forces!'

They stared at him, speechlessly.

'Haven't you seen the lights on in the village?' Ludi asked. Still no response. 'Haven't you anything to say?' he bawled in anger and frustration.

'We not watch village no more. Too much tired. Not much food,' said Suzuki, solemnly.

'Were you in prison?' Mary asked.

'Yes, Noguchi put me in!'

'How long have you been free?'

'I was let out when the first Americans arrived in the village, three days ago.'

'Three days ago! How very like you! Why didn't you come up to us? Why didn't you come up and tell us?' she asked, accusingly.

'I was sure that you would know. How could I imagine you wouldn't know? Everyone in the world knows.' Ludi looked helplessly from one face to another. 'I had to go to Tokyo. I was *ordered* to go there,' he added, sulkily.

Suzuki rose from her bed; deftly she straightened her kimono, put her sparse hair neatly in order. They watched her tensely as she sat in front of Ludi, feet neatly tucked beneath her.

'Hello, old lady,' Ludi grinned. 'Have you been eating?'

'Thank you, yes I have been eating. Then – it is true, Ludi Sama, war is all finished?'

'Yes. The war is finished.'

'My country – makimashitaka – beaten?'

'It is true, old woman.' He placed a kindly hand on her shoulder. She drew away, and went out of the house.

'Fancy her caring so much,' said Mary.

'Why shouldn't she care?' asked Ludi coldly. 'She is Japanese.'

'That,' said Mary passionately, 'is nothing to be proud of.'

'I disagree with you.'

'You hate the Japanese – you have said so a dozen times.'

'I have never said that. I like many Japanese – Suzuki San, especially.'

'You are two-faced, you always were!'

'And you are a cold woman! If you had any warmth in you, you would comfort the person who has stood by you, served you loyally.'

'*I* am not two-faced. I am glad Japan is beaten.' A smile of delight spread over Mary's face. 'I can't believe that peace has come. . . .'

'It hasn't!' Ludi said, wearily. 'There can't be peace while people like you are still full of vengeance, and of all the other ingredients that cause wars.'

'You always could annoy me, Ludi, but in future I shall refuse to be worried by you.'

'You and I have no future, Mrs Ogata.'

'I have a beautiful future.'

'What makes you so sure of that?'

'Mike and I are going to be married! We are going to be the happiest people. That's what makes me so sure.'

'And who is going to give the happy bride away? Goro Ogata – your husband?' Ludi ran his hand along his chin, deep in thought. 'I don't believe that Mike really wants to marry you,' he said.

'He does, he does! You shut up! He does. . . .'

Mike was looking out through the tattered paper window, his heart full, his thoughts far away from this mountain village. His parents, friends, so many friends, would rejoice in his return to them. . . .

133

'Do you, Mike?' Mary's touch on his shoulder brought him back to reality.

'Do I what?'

'You see? He doesn't!' Ludi was laughing.

'You do, don't you? Please Mike, make him stop.'

'Do I what? Make him stop what?' asked Mike.

'Do you really want to take Mary to be your wedded wife?' laughed Ludi.

'Of course.' Mike spoke vaguely.

'Whatever for?' Ludi demanded.

'Why,' asked Mike, 'do most men want to marry?'

Ludi spoke airily. 'For money, companionship, animal passion, and in some cases, love.' He paused. 'Oh, yes! And one other reason, the most dangerous one of all – gratitude.'

Mike's arm went around Mary. 'We won't tell him our reasons, honey, we'll just let him keep guessing. And you two! Are you actually quarrelling? Right now, when the war's over? You are nuts. Why can't we go down to the village? I've never seen it, and I'd better report my precious self to someone, so that news can be sent to my folks that I'm alive and kicking.'

'I think,' answered Ludi slowly, 'that, unless you want an avalanche of American hysteria on your shoulders, it will be better for you to take things quietly.'

'Seems you don't like Americans – or do you, Ludi?'

'Yes, sir! But I am not yet adjusted to American enthusiasm.'

'Well, you must admit that my case is rather unusual,' said Mike modestly.

Ludi smiled. 'Most unusual! Mike, you can do one of two things. Go to Tokyo tomorrow and report to Headquarters there, or you can go now to the village, down the track. There are no byways, you can't get lost, just go to the Mampei Hotel, ask to see one of the officers there.'

'What do you think I should do, Mary?' asked Mike.

'I leave it to you to decide.'

'Sweet docile thing!' Ludi grinned.

Ignoring him, she looked questioningly at Mike, who was

134

already putting Ludi's old shoes on, his heart beating with excitement. 'You don't mind, do you, honey, if I go without you?' he murmured.

'No,' Mary spoke slowly. 'I don't mind.'

'Then – let's go. Come on, Ludi.'

'I said you, not we,' Ludi said, firmly.

'But you *must* come! If it weren't for you, I wouldn't be here to tell my tale.'

'That's right, Mike! I did save you.'

'You sure did.'

'I deserve a reward, don't I?'

'Here it comes,' said Mary. 'I could have told you, Mike, that he rescued you because he knew the war was ending – you are Ludi's insurance.'

'Insurance? Reward! My family would do anything in the world for Ludi – for you too, Mary . . .'

'Only you can give me my reward,' interrupted Ludi. 'I want you to promise me never to mention, to anyone, my part in this business!'

'But why?' asked Mike, astounded.

'That will be my reward!'

'But how can I explain?'

'Just don't mention my name, or Suzuki San's either.'

'But *why*?'

'Suzuki San would hate it, and so would I.'

'How will I explain – what can I say?'

'As far as I'm concerned, you can say that you crawled up here, and Mrs Ogata took you in.'

'Tell me why I mustn't mention your name! I don't understand!'

'Certainly I'll tell you. The risk that I took for you *was* a kind of insurance – but not with your rich family, not with your rich army. Just with myself.'

'You are the strangest guy. You mean this?'

'Get going, Mike, get going.' Ludi gave him a friendly push.

'O.K., then. Man! what a shock some folk are going to get!'

Mike saluted, and, with a happy laugh, went into the night.

Ludi and Mary listened to his footsteps, as they had listened, so many times, to the sound of footsteps coming or going up the rough track.

'Now, if that had been me,' said Ludi crudely, 'I would have taken my girl with me.'

33

THE happiness that Mary had known with Mike was melting as snow melts in the early spring. This feeling of being rejected was a familiar one to her; she had known it from childhood.

'You look perturbed, Mary,' said Ludi. 'I don't blame you. I fear that you have a difficult row to hoe and I tremble for your future.'

'Tremble for your own future. Don't worry over mine.'

'I can't help myself!' He spoke in pseudo-sympathy. 'Once again, I see you living in the shadow of parental disfavour. I see Mike looking at you through the eyes of his Country Club Mother, who is, I imagine, full of prides and prejudices. Your past will not please her – I fear.'

Mary stared at him silently as he continued in a harsh voice. 'If you marry Mike, you'll have another "bado" marriage. As for Mike – well, he deserves a better fate!'

Could she find some way to hurt Ludi Hoffer? A way that he would never forget? He had the power to make her feel smaller than a dust mote; one word from him, a slight twist of his lips, was enough to crush any opinion she proffered, any dream she had. His outrageous self-confidence, his ego! If she could only flatten that! She must! She would find a way to humiliate him.

But to do that, she would have to be smart. She would need a little time, a little preparation.

Ludi was surprised when Mary suddenly smiled at him. There

she had sat, looking at him stolidly. He'd been sure that she was either about to cry or burst into a fury of rage, but there she was, smiling, and saying, 'Let's be friends, Ludi! Let's stop arguing!'

Warily he replied, 'You must want something very badly – what is it?'

She laughed. 'How smart you are! Yes, take me down to the village; I want to walk about in peace and freedom. What does it feel like? And maybe you could find me something to eat?'

'To eat! How long is it since you ate? I'm a thoughtless fool. Mary, you stay here; I'll run down to the village right now, and bring rations for you and Suzuki San. Poor old girl, still out there, alone.'

'Do that, we'll wait here – and about Suzuki San, I *am* fond of her, you do believe that, Ludi?'

'I believe you are. You're a nasty girl, but not all that nasty.'

They went out to the garden and Ludi listened as Mary spoke to the old woman.

'Don't be sad, Suzuki San,' she said gently.

'Must be sad.'

'Everything will be all right.'

'Japan not all right.'

Mary was not much of a comforter. He could do better. 'Old lady,' he said. 'Do you remember telling me how your grandmother spanked you when you were a little girl?'

'No,' said Suzuki glumly.

'Well you did tell me. She spanked you when you told her you had heard that Japan is only a little country in the world, and that there are many bigger countries. You remember?'

'Remember.'

'Your O-baa-san told you that Japan was a great big grand country.'

'She was wrong.'

'She was right. Any land that has people like you in it is a grand big country.'

'Me?'

'That's right! Your country has had a spanking. It will get over it, as you did, will remember it as you do. You can help it by believing your grandmother's story.'

Suzuki smiled. 'Ludi Sama, you talk very good.'

'Will you try and be more happy?'

'I try.'

'Good. I leave the house.'

'I await your return.' Suzuki bowed in the dark garden.

Ludi, on his way to the village, wondered whether Japan had been fully spanked – yet. There was a blank look in many Japanese eyes these last few days. Shame and horrified belief of war atrocities was pressing on the civilians of Japan like a heavy burden.

Passing the hotel, he noticed a milling crowd of men and officers, heard excited voices. Mike's big moment! Well, why not? Life didn't give a man many such moments.

Quickly he went to his quarters, to get food from the cook-sergeant still on duty there. 'Plenty of it – for some friends of mine.'

'Sure! Take what you want.'

Ludi filled his rucksack – a new American one – and added a bottle of whisky, a carton of cigarettes.

They would celebrate the peace, do it in style. After all, and he had to admit, it had been good seeing Mary again.

Hurrying past the hotel, he saw that although the time was nearly midnight, all lights were on and a crowd of men in uniform were drinking – cheering.

Glancing through the door, he saw Mike grinning happily, a glass held high in his one hand, and an army photographer was taking flashbulb shots of the scene.

Ludi could envisage the headlines – THE MIRACLE OF MIKE PETERS.

Well, they wouldn't be too far-fetched, at that.

34

Once more Ludi climbed the familiar path. At the turn of the track, Suzuki stood gazing out over the desolation of Japan. Let her have her little time to herself, different from the time that Mike was having – but hers.

He envied both of them, for he could have neither victory nor defeat, but was, as usual, on his own. Hadn't he always been on his own? He was used to it, but he felt the lack of belonging to anything, or to anybody, deeply enough to envy the glory of victory or even the misery of defeat.

Did he want to belong to something or to somebody? Yes, better by far than this impersonal emptiness. What did he hope to get out of life? He already had more than enough money to armour him against adversity – and yet he felt lonelier than he'd ever felt before.

What a fool he'd been, jeering at Mary, trying to make her stand up to things, face realities. He'd thought to strengthen her. But he had only, as Mike put it, 'knocked' her. That had never been his real intention. From the moment he had set eyes on her, heard her voice, he had admired her extreme femininity. Then why hadn't he been satisfied to admire the will-o'-the-wisp uncertainties of her mind?

He had wanted her soft loveliness to remain but with a decisive strength of mind as well. Why had he thought like that? He had always loathed women with decisive minds. He wanted a girl exactly as Mary was now. Exactly!

Was it too late? Never too late! He would tell her he loved her, tell her how, so many times, countless times, he'd desired her and how wrong he'd been in not telling her before. He'd dreamed many a time of the war being over, of such a time as this.

Well, the war was over, and how did she feel towards *him*? Let her be furious, let her be anything she wished, but let her be his. He would have to tread carefully, very softly.

He found her sitting on the tatami she disliked so much. 'What have you done to yourself?' he exclaimed.

'I've brushed my hair, changed into a dress, why?'

Surely no hair in the world had ever gleamed so golden, and just brushing hair couldn't make lips and cheeks so glowing and warm? 'You're beautiful!' he said.

'Of course I made up a little and even used the perfume I'd forgotten I owned. Here, sniff!' She leaned towards him.

He sniffed, delicious! But go softly, 'You are beautiful!' he repeated.

'You're not so bad yourself. But Ludi . . .?'

'Umm?'

'Did you bring something to eat?'

'Surely, and a bottle of bourbon. He poured whisky into the tea-bowls that they had used many times before. 'I like these bowls; may I keep them, Mary?'

'Keep them, I hate them.' She downed the whisky without a shudder.

'Try a chicken leg, Mary!' He would take some to Suzuki San; he mustn't neglect that.

Mary dug her teeth in with enthusiasm. 'Pour me another drink, Ludi. Remember the rice cakes, that day at the police station?'

'Sure. Poor old Noguchi! I saw him yesterday. He asked me to tell him why we – er – murdered Captain Tanaka.'

'Let's have another drink, Ludi. Did you tell him?' She grinned at him like a mischievous schoolgirl.

'To his profound disappointment, I did not.'

'I should think not! Now! I feel fine. I can't believe I feel so fine.'

Was it only the food and whisky making her feel as she did? Was it possible that so suddenly she could speak to him in this warm way? It was what he wanted, but wasn't it just too good to be true?

She was pouring another drink and he remembered now that she had told him that whisky always made her ill. 'Mary! Take it easy,' he advised.

'Take it easy? Why, I'd like to drink the bottle dry, run up to the top of the volcano, shout out how glad I am that the war is over. That's how I feel, but I don't want to be sick, so I'll take your advice.' She did dislike whisky, but would encourage Ludi to drink more. He should be hand-fed the way country people feed geese before killing them for a feast. Was he suspicious? 'Let's talk of only nice things, huh?' she said.

'Suits me. Anything you say. It's queer the way everything has turned out. Does it ever worry you that we killed old Tanaka?'

'Do you call that a nice subject? I don't. No – I don't think that it will ever worry me. Does it worry you?'

'Not in the least.' Truthfully, it did worry him. He wished that it had not happened. But forget the past. . . . He found it difficult to take his eyes, his mind, away from this laughing-faced Mary; this was the way he wanted her to look.

'Mary, were you hurt because Mike walked out like that?' he asked, and his voice was gentle.

She looked at her hands; the scars left from Captain Tanaka's cigarette-burns were still vivid; they would never completely fade. 'Hurt! I felt piqued, but hurt? No, not exactly.'

'He'll be back,' said Ludi tentatively.

'I would still go on living if he didn't come back.'

'Do you mean that?'

'Mean what, Ludi?'

He looked intently into the eyes so close to his. 'That you don't really care as much for Mike as you have had me believing?'

'How serious are you! Don't look so serious. How can it matter to you, the way I feel about Mike? It couldn't matter to you.'

'It could – it does matter.'

'I can't imagine why, for you've always thought less than the dust of me.'

'That's not true!'

'You have, you know that you have, Ludi.' Rising, she stood by the window.

Hands on her shoulders, he swung her about to face him.

'You've never understood me . . .' he said and his voice was strained. 'But, Mary, I've always understood you.'

Her plan, revenge, working out so smoothly, but she must remain on guard. He was going to take her in his arms. Fine, for this was her intention, but not yet. She needed time, for if he were to hear, feel, the thumping drum that her heart had become, it would spoil her plan. She needed time and strength to do combat not only against Ludi Hoffer, but against herself, standing by the torn paper window, with misty, half-closed eyes and filled with turbulent, treacherous desires.

This wasn't what she'd intended. Think about Mike – that would help. Fleetingly she called Mike to mind, but Ludi, taller, darker, more demanding than Mike could ever be, blotted out the image.

And those arms of hers—traitors! Of their own accord, they clasped, wantonly, about his neck and the hands of Ludi Hoffer roamed at will, burning where they touched.

She had grown accustomed to being burnt; it always hurt, but this was maddening pain, a purgatory with a promise of heaven. Was she strong enough to give up a trip to heaven? If she could keep in mind that it was to be only a trip and, later, do as planned. *That* should not be so difficult, for this mouth on hers was the mouth of Ludi Hoffer, and the only thing to do was to remember that the man who had so easily, effortlessly, carried her to this bed on the floor was the one and same Ludi who . . .

What was it she must remember? Nothing, for there had never been anything before this. At the end of this dark warm road, there was treasure, a something never before experienced, and this was the road leading to a place where one could never go alone. She was, for the first time in her life – not alone; and how sharply bright, star-bright, it was away there in the dim distance.

How mysterious to clamour and yearn to reach that brightness and at the same time, frantically to hope that the journey would never end, never be finished . . . It was enough to make her cry out. Not only that, but to weep, have tears gush from her eyes, because, horrifyingly, for an instant, she was left solitary, and this was not to be endured. Wildly she reached out, and was gathered close with a strength and tenderness unimagined ever before in her life, or in her life's most secret dreams.

This was not dreaming, or enduring, but living in darkness, suddenly darkened, and this new sudden longing to give and to take was a pain of pure delight. . . . She now desired only to lie in this black-velvet moat among the stars.

35

THERE had been many girls and women in Ludi's life. Some he remembered with pleasure, but usually he had regretted the ease of his conquests, searching always for the feminine creature who would cause him arduous, difficult chase. There had been many pursuits, but he had been aware, always, that it was a game played, in some cases, with finesse, but with the end of the story known to both, at the beginning.

He had been prepared for lengthy battle, for the conquest of Mary, and to have it all so quickly accomplished had caused his mind to lurch with disappointment. Her hasty passion, her acceptance of him, so unexpected, affected him strangely. Perhaps the ideal quality he had searched for in women existed only in his own longing imagination, and perhaps in the minds and hearts of all men.

This, then, was to be the old story retold? Well! What if it was? It was a gigantic necessary slice of life.

He despised himself, he deserved to be hung by the neck for dragging Mary through such emotional, physical, exertion. How lovely her body, and how anxious. If he were to end that anxiety, satisfy the urge his selfishness had caused, then, by all means, better attempt to forget that this girl lying with him was Mary, spoiler of his dream. Make believe, let her be just any girl.

But he had always despised pretence in any form and realised that she was suddenly aware of the situation and was surmising his thoughts. He also became aware that, no matter what experiences she had gone through, she had never known passion fulfilled. That knowledge drenched out the past. Life began anew with a beginning-of-the-world newness, and he felt that there could never again be any other woman to fulfil the dream, the whole desire, of his body and heart – especially of his heart. He would think only of her, of ways to enchant, and then the awareness that she, innocently, beautifully, was thinking of his well-being, filled him with a happiness that was almost sorrowful.

He lay, afraid to breathe deeply, lest the sound disturb the peace that his love had achieved in the girl by his side, this girl who, because of his clumsy imperceptiveness, he had so nearly lost. Let him never forget the way he felt towards her at this moment; show her, for all the days of her life, nothing but good things. See her smile, hear her laugh, head thrown back – in the sunlight, the moonlight.

The moon, as though responsive to his thoughts, filled the shabby room with its pale light and he looked down at her, took her hand gently, and was amazed at the tenderness of his own lips against it.

Touching her mouth tentatively with his finger, he pleaded, 'Smile, Mary – you've been sleepy long enough.'

It was such a puzzled little smile that he laughed triumphantly, and to end the doubt that he saw in it, he whispered, 'I love you! Do you know that for the remainder of your life no other man is to be allowed to as much as touch you. To hell with them all, to hell with Mike, with . . .'

What had caused her to spring up as though a scorpion were in the bed? Why was she looking down at him, that expression on her face?

The room was full of moonlight, and Mary hurriedly draped a kimono about her nakedness, Mike's name had seeped like a poison into her mind. Her brain swayed with puzzlement. . . . What had she intended to do?

144

She remembered and, against every true instinct, fought a battle that she was determined to win; even though, in the winning, she would taste the bitterness that victory can, and does at times, deal out to the victorious.

Stepping back, preparing for battle, Mary laughed and to her own ears it was an ugly sound. 'Now, I know,' she said.

Ludi caught at her hand, pulled her towards the bed. She resisted, pulled away from him.

'Know what, Mary?'

Like a puppet she obeyed some evil master and could not prevent the words coming from her mouth. 'I know now what it is to be loved by, to be made love to, by . . .'

'By?'

'. . . by a street woman's bastard son!'

'And how was it?' asked Ludi, gently.

'It was disgusting,' she whispered.

'Surely not disgusting?'

'It was *disgusting*!'

Ludi closed his eyes for an instant, then rose, put on his clothes, and walked from the house.

Mary watched from the window, as Suzuki came out into the moonlight from the shadows of the trees at the edge of the garden. The old woman caught at Ludi's hand; they spoke for a brief moment, then he walked on down the mountain path.

The door slid open, Suzuki pulled the dangling light-cord, and the harsh light killed the shadowy moonlight. There was an expression in the older woman's eyes that caused Mary to shrink back a little from the weary critical disillusionment etched on the wrinkled face; it could have been that the old woman had been an eyewitness of what had just happened in the room.

Suzuki's sigh, echoing, seemed to float, seeking a place to settle. Her voice, when at last she spoke, was cold. 'War over now, Mary Sama. Suzuki leave you now – in the morning – early.' Politely she added, 'Gooda-nighto!'

'Good night, good night, Suzuki San,' whispered Mary.

She looked again out of the window into the moonlight. In

the crisp air she distantly heard Ludi's footfalls, going down the steep track, out of her life – and she knew that she loved Ludi Hoffer.

In this small Japanese house she had committed not one murder, but two; and the murder of Captain Tanaka was as nothing compared with the crime she had committed in deliberately murdering love.

Part Two

THE OCCUPATION

36

News of Mike's miraculous escape was causing more excitement than he had expected. War correspondents thronged around him. He smiled, posed and answered vaguely, 'Yes, I realise my good fortune. Yes, my parents will be overjoyed. Yes, I'll arrange an interview with my rescuers. When? As soon as possible; but they want no publicity. . . .'

'They must be grand people, Lieutenant.'

'They are,' answered Mike fervently. Why had Ludi put a ban on the telling of his part? He realised that Suzuki San naturally would resent being caught up in this fuss; and he found it impossible to bring Mary's name into his story. Was it because she was still married to a Japanese? Mike wanted her to get her divorce quietly, so that he could take her back to the States with him, avoiding publicity of her Japanese marriage.

At noon the following day he was still at the hotel, freshly bathed and shaven, the sleeve of his new uniform neatly pinned up; the world of fear and tension seemed far away. He leant against the bar, a crowd of interested men about him, and, in his hand, a cable from San Francisco.

'Don't open it yet, Peters. Let's get a shot of Peters opening this cable from his folks.'

'Can we know what the cable says, Lieutenant?'

Mike found it difficult to open; he fumbled. 'Let me help you do that, Lieutenant.' Ready hands opened the envelope. His eyes were misty as he read: it was from his parents and he stuffed it in his pocket. He would read it again later in private.

'Who are you giving the rights of your story to, Lieutenant?'

'There's a bundle of green stuff in your story, Lieutenant.'

'We want you to get ready to leave for Tokyo.'

'Tokyo, when?'

'Why, right now. This village is only a backwater. Things will really start popping in Tokyo. . . .'

'I would like to have some free time. Some things I would like to do . . .'

'Come now, Lieutenant, don't hold out on us. Tell us the names of the people you owe your life to. No? Well, you are not going to be out of our sight for one moment. How d'you like that? How 'bout that, Lieutenant?'

'You could give a guy a break,' smiled Mike.

'That is what we have been asking you for, Lieutenant – a break.'

'No dice,' said Mike.

'Be a buddy. We have a living to make.'

What, thought Mike, am I going to do? Blast Ludi and his false modesty. Across the room he saw the very man he was blasting looking at him over the heads of his admirers.

Mike made a move, but Ludi was quicker. A grin on his face, he turned, hands clasped over his head, a signal of victory. 'You can have it on your own, boy!' Mike read these words on Ludi's face.

When Ludi disappeared from sight, he had a moment of loneliness and depression quite overwhelming. Quickly he made up his mind. The men's toilet! The only place where he could have privacy. Kneeling on the tiled floor, he placed a piece of notepaper on the seat.

The short note asked Mary to understand, to wait in the little house for him. He would return as soon as he could, but if he was longer than three days she was to come to Tokyo. He named a building he had been told of in Tokyo, the Dai Ichi, he spelt it Die Itchy and it looked damned strange but that was the name of the place he had been told of. He would leave a message for her there; he would wait for her, he wrote.

At the reception desk he wrote Ludi's name on the envelope, adding, *Please deliver this to Mary.* He sealed and put it on a bracket, where he noticed that a steady stream of men came and went, leaving and picking up chits.

A few hours later, Mike was in sprawling, humid, bombed-out Tokyo city, where, for three days, he was fêted, photographed, interviewed, examined.

He chose to have medical attention in Japan. 'I prefer it. No, I would really prefer it to flying home immediately.'

'Is there anything we can do for you, Lieutenant? Anything at all – just let us know. . . .'

'Nothing, thank you.'

A few days later, his father walked into the lobby of Mike's hotel. Camera lights flashed. 'How 'bout that, Lieutenant! Some surprise, huh!'

Above the din Mike smiled into his father's eyes. 'Hi, Dad!'

Mike senior's pleasant face was oddly contorted. 'Hullo, Mike!' he said, nearer to tears than he had been since childhood. His son – alive, and that empty sleeve.

That evening the father and son were alone together.

'Mike, I was told today that we can leave for home as soon as we wish. Your mother broke down completely when we heard we had lost you. She's waiting.'

'I know, Dad, I want to see her. How I want to see her. . . .'

'Then, what's stopping us?'

His parents would be against his marriage to Mary, a divorced woman, a girl who had married a Japanese. So different from the Country Club set girls he had grown up among. He knew that his mother had set her heart on his marrying her closest friend's daughter. He, at one time, had vaguely entertained the same idea.

Restlessly, uneasily, he now knew that he would never marry that girl. Never, no matter what happened.

'Mike?' His father was waiting.

Mike told him the story of his rescue, told it well. The older man was able to see Ludi, Mary and Suzuki. He saw his son's body dragged up a ladder-like staircase, dumped on the floor of a dark Japanese attic, brawny Ludi crouching over, protecting him. He could not wait to meet that man.

He saw blood gush from the legs of the old woman, and resolved to dilute his bitterness against the Japanese a little.

He heard the animal screams of a Japanese policeman as a fair-haired girl plunged sharp scissors again and again into his body. He covered his eyes with his hand; Mike saw that his father was crying.

'It's all over now, Dad. But you can imagine how I feel, I just can't rush off without a word.'

'I understand.'

'Dad, I'm going to marry Mary Ogata.'

'Mary – who? I thought you said she is an American girl?'

'She is, she is married to a Japanese – a chemist, a scientist, I'm not quite sure what he does.'

'She is – married, to a . . . married? How can you marry a married woman?'

Mike felt irritation flow over him; he spoke impatiently. 'Look, Dad, I am a big boy now, I've been through quite a bit.'

'I know. I know that, but you mustn't rush into things.'

'Who's rushing?' asked Mike.

'I'm sorry. Go on with your story.'

Mike carefully spaced his words, as one would when speaking to a child. 'Mary is getting a divorce. Her marriage was never happy. . . . There is nothing left of it. She is a lovely girl. She saved my life. She never had happiness. Her father, he lives in San Francisco, he was rotten to her . . .'

'What is his name?'

'I – don't know!'

The boy needed careful handling; he'd been through a lot. Humour him. 'Go on, son. I see.'

'Well, Dad, I want to stay here, wait till Mary's free, marry her here, take her home as my wife.'

'I see.'

'What the hell is it you see?'

'Perhaps I don't see; be patient with me. We, your mother and I, have always hoped . . . Just be patient with me. When can I meet her?'

'Meet who?' asked Mike truculently.

Mike Senior cleared his throat and smiled. 'Mary, your girl.'

'That's better.' Mike smiled back at the best father in the

world. 'You'll love her, I know.' But he had never been less sure of anything.

'We can see her tomorrow; she is waiting for me in that house I have been telling you about. Will you come?'

'Try and stop me,' his father said, in a strangely determined voice.

37

'LUDI,' said Stephen Barnes, 'I want you to come to Provost H.Q. in Tokyo. I like the way we work together.'

Ludi thought for a moment. 'Have you finished here in the village?'

'There's plenty to be cleaned up here still, but I've been given a more important job. I'll be quartered in Tokyo – like to have you along.'

'I don't know. I have plans, I'm going to start a business in Japan.' He had not until this moment known that this was what he intended to do.

'Are you in so great a rush to get started in business?' smiled Barnes.

'I'm in no rush at all.'

'O.K., then?'

'O.K.!'

'By the way, I brought a message for you; found it in the rack at the hotel.' He handed to Ludi, Mike's note. 'Who, if I may ask, is Mary?'

'I haven't the faintest idea.' Ludi slowly tore the letter in half, and then into small fragments.

Barnes spoke admiringly. 'Aren't you curious? I could never do a thing like that.'

'I'm no bell-hop!' said Ludi, tossing the scraps into a trash basket.

'Are you warning me?' laughingly asked Barnes.

'Could be.'

The American captain was caught up in the warmth of Ludi's smile. 'Shall we go and get high and happy?' he asked.

'Really high and happy?'

'Stinking.'

'I,' said Ludi, 'am your man.'

38

MARY paused at the look-out and looked back at the village. It was alive, free, and even gay. She went on up to the house, and placed on the floor the rations she had collected. Elbows on the low sill, she sat beside the window. The paper still fluttered in strips. 'Why don't you fix it?' Goro had asked. She raised her hands and ripped the tattered paper down, crushed it into a ball, tossed it outside.

Goro Ogata had made no effort to find out if she were alive or dead. As far as he knew, she could be penniless. Her father! No use in pretending that he held any interest in her. Suzuki San, true to her word, had packed her brown bag and had gone, Mary didn't know where. There was no word from Mike. Did he intend to ignore her? Did things like this happen to other people?

Desolately she thought of Ludi, and she had no courage to remember further . . . also, footsteps were heard coming up the track. From habit, her heart-beat quickened; then, remembering that there was no need to fear footsteps any more, she watched as Mike, and a grey-haired man, drew near the house.

Mike's father saw a slender girl with ungroomed hair, dressed in a blouse and shabby slacks. He looked into the face of the girl, and saw an expression of relief pass over it. This girl was not too sure of Mike. . . .

'Mike, I'm so glad to see you again!'

'Me, too.' Mike kissed her cheek. 'You got my note?' he asked. 'I left it for Ludi to take care of.'

'I got no note. Ludi has not been here since . . .'

'I'm here now, honey; let's go inside. Come on, Dad.' How to make up to Mary? His neglect of her had been wrong. 'I was taken to Tokyo,' he explained, lamely. 'I was sure that you would get my note.'

Mike Senior looked around the dim little room. The girl was not even trying to make a good impression on him. She had given him a startled look and murmured, 'Won't you sit down?' and she had sat on the floor. Mike Junior also sat on the floor. On the floor! Mike Senior stood uneasily. Why didn't his son help out, say something? He was indignant that the girl Mike wanted to marry could have let herself get into such a state. The women in his family – so fastidious – he could not imagine one woman or girl of his acquaintance looking so tacky. But he was being unfair, for this girl had suffered great hardships; he must remember that. She had killed a man to save young Mike's life. His son had told a wonderful tale of this girl; he must be fair.

Mike Senior looked at her again, determined to find those qualities his son had told him of. He could not imagine a laugh of any kind coming from those nervous lips, and she kept examining her hands as though she found something distasteful on them. She looked up and met his eyes; and then hastily moved her hands. Good Lord, she was sitting on them! Was this the girl Mike was going to bring back and present to his loving, but very social mother? Now she was looking intently at Mike Junior. Someone had to speak. 'Well, Mary!' he said and he heard the strained artificiality of his voice.

'I am sorry that I look like this,' she whispered.

'Like what?' Mike's voice was hard – it could have been Ludi speaking. 'You look darling to me,' he said, and took one of her hands and held it gently.

She smiled at him, but pulled her hand away to tuck it back into its hiding place. Rebuffed, Mike looked about the room and a thought struck him. 'Where is Suzuki San? Dad, you have to meet Suzuki San, she is the greatest . . .'

'She went away,' said Mary.

'But why? She thought the world of you, I can't believe it. I just have to see her again, I want to do so much for her.' His voice trailed into silence.

'Well, we can't stay here for ever.' Mike Senior was decisive. 'Pack your bag, Mary; we are taking you out of this.' He spoke kindly. 'I want to see you prettied up. I want to see you as you really are.'

'Mr Peters,' said Mary. 'Please sit down – on the floor – we have no chairs.' She continued, 'I'm glad you came here today.' A smile touched her lips and he glimpsed the beauty Mike had spoken of. 'I'm very glad you came, Mike.'

'I should hope so,' said Mike. 'I'll give Ludi hell when I see him, the louse, not delivering my message.'

'That will be something,' said Mary. 'You, giving Ludi hell.' They laughed together. She is beautiful, decided the father.

'I'm glad you both came,' continued Mary, 'because you have helped me to make up my mind.' She turned to the younger man. 'You don't love me – not really, do you, Mike?'

'I do – I always will.'

'I'm glad to know that, Mike! I want you always to love me; and, this way, I think you will.'

'Which way?'

'You go your way, I go mine. Mike, we are very alike, we would make a hopeless married couple.'

'You don't know what you are saying . . .'

'I know, and you know. We were here together, lonely, frightened; we turned to each other for comfort – or, rather, I turned to you.'

'Was that all, Mary?'

'Certainly. Mike, you have never even kissed me – I mean not really.'

They were silent a moment, their eyes met and laughter rang out in the dim old room. 'Well, we were half-starved,' cried Mike, apologetically. 'But I do love you, Mary,' and he took her hand again.

'Like a sister,' she teased.

'More, much more than a sister!'

'That's nice,' she smiled. 'You were going to marry me out of gratitude. Someone once said that that is a deadly reason for marriage.'

'Ludi said that!'

'Sssh! Mike, I agreed to be your wife because I long for the normal good things of life. You would be my second escape from misery. You know that's true? Admit the truth, Mike! Don't leave it all to me.'

A load moved off his mind. He could now do – as he had been afraid to admit even to himself – that thing he longed to do. 'You're saying it, Mary,' he murmured. He had always been a very nice young man, and he tried not to let the excitement and happiness in his heart spread to his face. His thoughts were racing wildly. This was the starting point in his search for Yuriko.

39

MARY had decided to part from Mike and his father at Tokyo railroad station, but the milling crowds, the heat, and the fetid air of the devastated city, hit her nostrils unpleasantly, made her nervous.

They pushed their way through the unruly noisy mob of soldiers from Australia, from Britain, white and coloured Americans, and dejected Japanese civilians.

Sleek, well-tailored girls of the Occupation Forces wiggled their way through the male crowd with feminine confidence. They were at a premium and aware of that fact. Japanese girls, such as Mary had not known to exist, brazenly clung to the arms of soldiers. Catching Mary's look of amazement, Mike yelled, 'General MacArthur has closed down the Yoshiwara.'

'What did you say?'

'I said – the brothels have been closed down!'

'Man! They sure have!' a gigantic Texan drawled. 'All this, and all for a bar of chocolate!' He was a fine-looking man and wore a captain's uniform. Giving Mike a resounding thump on the back, he went his way laughing heartily.

Mike Senior said in disgust, 'Let's get out of this.'

After a long wait they found a war-wearied taxi. 'I want you to drop me off at Red Cross Headquarters,' said Mary. 'I'm getting myself a job there; I want to wear one of those divine uniforms.'

'You, my dear Mary,' said Mike Senior, 'want nothing of the sort; you need feeding up, and you need rest, care . . .'

Now that he was sure that Mike was free, Mary's virtues were apparent to him. He wanted to take great care of her.

'You just come in and recommend me,' continued Mary. 'I want nothing less, nothing more.'

A position at Red Cross H.Q. was quickly found; Mary was a welcome addition to the staff, her knowledge of Japanese making her invaluable. She was to be interpreter for grim-faced, frighteningly competent, Amelia Francis. She was given a neat cubicle, one of the divine uniforms, and a make-up kit.

Mike and his father waited patiently for her, and, when Mary at last appeared before them, she was as sleek and well-tailored as her sisters; but after they said good-bye, Mike turned back and watched Mary. 'I feel as though I have thrown her to the wolves, Dad! I feel rotten.'

'Now, Mike! You have nothing to reproach yourself with. Mary is a lovely girl.'

'You don't say!'

'Now, Mike, don't be disrespectful . . .'

'Sorry, Dad.'

'That's O.K., son.'

Back in the hotel room, Mike Senior sat relaxed and happy. Thank God *that* was over! Wait till the boy's mother heard of what he had saved her son from. He couldn't wait to get home –

out of this madhouse – couldn't wait to tell her. 'Mike,' he called.

Mike stuck his head out from the bathroom door. 'Yes, Dad?'

'How's about it, that we leave Japan tomorrow – your mother will be getting frantic.'

'I can't go. Not yet.'

'Now, break it up, why can't you come?'

'I,' said Mike firmly, 'can't leave Japan yet, because I have to find my girl.'

'Find your . . .?'

'Dad – this will come as a shock to you. I'm in love, or I think I am, and I have to find out.'

'What the hell are you talking about?' Mike Senior sat back in utter perplexity.

'A girl I know – a girl I met in the village . . .'

'Another girl in the village! All the time we were sorrowing over you, breaking our hearts. Your mother's hair has turned grey over you. All this time you were being a blasted Don Juan.' Mike Senior was angry now; he was not accustomed to being thwarted. 'Pull yourself together, Mike – you are coming home.'

Mike looked kindly at his father. 'I'm sorry, Dad, but I've got to find her!'

'Who is this girl?'

'She is a Japanese girl. I'll never rest until I find her.'

'A Japanese girl! Hell! And then what?'

'If, and when, I find her, if she is as I remember her to be – now, Dad, don't look like that! If she will have me, I am going to marry her!'

His father stood to his feet, and spoke bitterly. 'I had rather you had died.'

They argued hotly. Exhausted at last, Mike Senior threatened, 'I am leaving here tomorrow. You won't come?'

Receiving no answer, he continued, 'Right! I'll inform your superiors of what you have in mind. There's a law against fraternisation. You'll find yourself in trouble – shipped home not in glory but in disgrace.'

'Do your damndest,' said Mike coldly. 'I know a thing or two.'

159

'That's your last word?'

'If that is your attitude, yes!'

'Then – good-bye.'

'No, Dad, not like this . . .' He held out his hand.

It was ignored. 'I told you, and I meant it, Mike, I would rather you had died.'

Mike lay on the bed; he was glad that his father had gone. Tomorrow he would start looking – for Yuriko!

Three days later he was standing outside a tall bamboo fence. In the pleasant house behind the fence he had been assured that Yuriko Noguchi lived. What was he to do now? He could not walk up, knock on the door and ask for Miss Noguchi. That would be tactless. He must see her alone.

Japanese people looked at him curiously as they passed by. This was a quiet part of the city; no member of the Occupation Forces had any business here. He strolled slowly away; he strolled back. This continued for an hour; he couldn't keep it up much longer.

An elderly man slid open the gate, stepped into the street, and walked in a dignified manner away from the house. Could that be the dreaded Noguchi? Was that the man who had been after him, not knowing, as Ludi had said, exactly what it was he had been looking for. And here I am, thought Mike, standing outside your very gate, but I know what *I* am looking for. He laughed as he watched the serious-looking man disappearing around the corner.

Two women came around the same corner and walked up the street towards him. The elderly woman gave him a hard look as he passed by; the younger stopped suddenly, stumbled a little, and walked on.

Yuriko! She had seen him. He finished his promenade to the corner. What should he do now? That look of delighted astonishment in her eyes! Her companion – her aunt, he supposed – had been unaware of anything unusual.

Crossing the road, he waited, but the wooden door remained

closed. He was about to take another stroll when the door opened. Yuriko came into the street, stood for a moment, looking about her; their eyes met across the road; he took a hasty step, she shook her head slightly and walked away. He followed, and it was like following a dream.

Not once did she glance over her shoulder. She went in through a gate, to a small park. He followed, but it wasn't a park; it was a Buddhist cemetery. Incense drifted in frail spirals from several of the strangely marked graves, and an old Japanese woman turned a wooden prayer-wheel in her hands. Taking no notice of the two young people, she continued mumbling her prayers.

Yuriko and Mike stood face to face. Neither moved, and neither spoke a word. In the dark almond eyes of the girl who stood looking at him, Mike saw what he wanted to know.

He held out his hand; her face brightened. 'Did you mean it when you said you would die for me?' he demanded.

She nodded her head.

Old woman at her prayers – it didn't matter, nothing mattered, the entire world could have been watching.

Mike took a step and caught his girl to him. He had held other girls – not like this! He had kissed other girls – not like this!

40

FOR over a month Mary had been living and working in Tokyo. The clean bright enthusiasm of the Allied Forces was like a frosting covering a cake that had burnt, sunk in the middle.

It was a bewildering time for both conquerors and conquered. The Americans had fought long and bloody battles against these people, had entered Japan with hearts stalwart, and ready for anything. The victorious soldiers looked about them at the shabby, down-trodden, depressed Japanese population, and in many cases began to adopt a benevolent attitude towards them. Japanese children could be seen hanging to the hands of these givers of chewing-gum and 'chocolato'; many Japanese families had 'American guests' in their homes, and 'K' rations became a familiar sight in many a Japanese kitchen.

The Japanese civilians had been bombed out of their homes, and had lived in hunger and suffering. They had been fed a propaganda of lies and truth, exaggerations and underestimations.

Instead of the bullying iron heel of the conqueror they had awaited, it was bewildering to find that this was not so. Conditions began to improve. Water flowed into kitchen and bathroom taps again, gas pipes once again fed gas into kitchen stoves. More rice than had been seen for many a year found its way into those same kitchens and, as the kitchen conditions of the nation improved, so did that nation's morale.

The great Allied Occupation machine, working with precision, weeding out 'war criminals,' sorting out problems far above the understanding of the common people, was scarcely noticed. The general opinion in Tokyo, among the man in the street, the woman in the kitchen, was that things could have been very much worse.

In many homes where soldiers came bringing their rations, Japanese families offered their guests the finest gifts possible. Everyone was weary of war. Both sides, glad that it was all over, accepted things as they were.

To prevent disease spreading, truckloads of American G.I.s would roar into a narrow twisting street, and with spray guns, D.D.T. the houses and people, or give typhus injections. Sometimes these occasions became rather gay, and the laughter of conquerors and conquered could be heard mingling.

There were diehards on both sides – many Jap-haters, and many a bitter Japanese who resented the Cccupation of his country. These two factions looked with disgust at their more easy-going brothers and sisters, but they were ignored, even laughed at.

Mary concentrated on her work, slept in the cubicle provided for her, ate the excellent food served at all meals. She made no special friend. The girls and women she worked with had come through a very different war to the one that she had lived through. They found it difficult to understand Mary; and she could find little in common with them.

She became accustomed to 'wolf whistles.' The Occupation soldiers, most of them at a loose end, strolled the streets in droves. They felt it their bounden duty to whistle at all and sundry pretty girls – not only pretty ones. Miss Francis reminded Mary of a tall, very thin horse; but Miss Francis received her share of whistles.

'Impertinent creatures – hanging about, behaving so badly. Why don't they use the recreations we take so much trouble to supply them with?'

'Oh, Miss Francis, they can't play table tennis all the time,' laughed Mary. 'They mean no harm.'

'Just be alone with one of them for a while, you would maybe think differently.'

'What would he do?' asked Mary, slyly.

Miss Francis looked sternly at Mary as though appraising her, wondering if she were old enough to hear the truth. 'Well, Mary, Lieutenant Williams told me, only yesterday, that some of his men are receiving penicillin shots for – well – you know what!'

'No,' said Mary wickedly. 'Tell me?'

Miss Francis put her mouth close to Mary's ear. 'For V.D.,' she hissed.

'How awful!'

'That's why I say it would be better for them to use our recreations more.'

Mike had called Mary on the phone several times.

'Have you another girl yet?' she had teased.

'Dozens of them.'

'Nicer than me?'

'Only one.'

'May I meet her?'

'I'm kidding you, Mary.' But she wondered.

At night she would sit alone in the lounge at the Red Cross hostel, reading magazines, watching girls wait for their dates to arrive. There were so few American girls, so many men. Some of the girls had three or four dates in one evening. Mary was amazed at their conceit in believing that it was their charms alone that gave them this giddying popularity.

'Why don't you come along?' the girls would ask her in the friendliest manner.

'I just don't want to.' Eventually they stopped asking her. She was different – forget her.

One Sunday she went to Azabu, the suburb of her former home with the Ogatas. She knew that they had moved to another house in that district after their home was burnt; but neighbours would tell her how to contact Goro.

Walking along the familiar streets, she hoped that he would not cause any delay about their divorce. She stood looking at the house in which, as she was told, she would find him. Someone was peering at her through a small window.

The door opened and a pair of hostile feminine eyes looked into hers; the same eyes, she was certain, that had peered through the window. 'Is Ogata Goro San living here?' she inquired in Japanese.

'Wait.' The young woman disappeared. She was pleasant, studious-looking; definitely not a servant. Hearing voices, Mary strained her ears to listen.

'*She* is here,' said the woman.

'Who?' asked Goro.

'*That* one.'

They came to the door together.

'Mary!' Goro was quite self-possessed. 'Dozo, dozo – please come inside.'

They sat down. 'Will you bring tea?' he asked the woman.

'Who is she, Goro? What a clever face she has!'

'She is clever and very pleasant. She is a biochemist, like myself.' He spoke quickly. 'Mary, I must tell you that I have started a divorce; I am going to marry again, that girl. We are suited to each other; we are having a child. I hope you don't mind . . .?'

Mary smiled wryly. If any woman should suffer from an inferiority complex, she was that woman. 'Goro, I think that it would have been pleasant if you had inquired into my well-being.'

He spoke hastily. 'Mary, don't be annoyed. I knew that I was just a convenience to you, an escape from your unhappy life. Isn't that the truth?'

'It's true,' she admitted.

'If you had tried to meet my parents even quarter way, things perhaps could have been different. Tell me, Mary, why have you come here today? Misa is upset, she thinks maybe you want to come back to me.'

She was silent. Let him squirm just a little. He was a kindly man, but . . .

He was looking at her in distress. 'You don't, do you?'

She laughed. 'I came to ask you to arrange a divorce!' The relief on his face was comical.

That evening she sat in the lobby thumbing through a new magazine. It seemed that no one on earth cared about her. Jumping to her feet she called to one of the girls: 'Where are you going tonight?'

'To a party.'

'Could I, may I . . .?'

'Sure! Climb on the wagon, honey-bun; there's plenty of room to spare and more. It's time you took some of the weight off us gals.'

41

As time went by a new element appeared in the gay night life of Tokyo. Japanese girls, not brazen but well-mannered, shy and well-educated, were escorted by men of the Occupation Forces who defied the orders prohibiting what was called 'fraternising' with the defeated enemy. Wherever one looked these days one could see G.I. Joe and his kimono'd girl friend.

Sometimes, now, some of the American girls at the Red Cross hostel sat in the lobby thumbing through magazines, hopefully waiting in vain for the phone to ring.

Mary was never left on the shelf. She had built a reputation for herself as a lively and witty girl. When asked why she refused to sleep with any of her many admirers, she would quote Miss Francis and the warning given her by that admirable lady on the supposed prevalence of V.D. among the men in the Forces.

Night after night she danced, sat in smoke-filled clubs, listened to talk that meant little to her – and watched hopefully for Ludi. She had no hope that he would forgive her, but if she could see him again it might help to erase from her memory that look of utter dismay that she had seen on his face that time when an evil spirit had made her say the thing to him that he could never forgive her for having said.

One night she went to the door of the hostel, and looked out into the street; her lieutenant was late. She shivered as she waited, for autumn had arrived. A G.I. Joe and his girl went by, holding hands. This Joe had but one arm; it was Mike Peters! She hadn't heard from him for weeks.

'Mike! It's me, Mary,' she called, and, running to him, threw her arms about his neck. He was delighted. 'Mary, how wonderful. It is you.'

'I thought you must have gone home, Mike.'

'Without saying good-bye to you? I'd never do that, Mary!'

'You might at least call me on the phone sometimes. Why haven't you?'

'This,' said Mike, taking the hand of his companion, 'is the reason. You two have met before.'

Recognition dawned. 'It's Noguchi's daughter!' Mary gasped.

'It,' said Mike warningly, 'is my girl.'

'I can't believe it! Does her father know? It's the strangest, the most . . .'

'Yuriko can talk, Mary. Why don't you stop saying "it" and "her." She is waiting to say hello to you.'

'Give me a moment. I'm flabbergasted – let's go somewhere and talk.'

'Have you time to spare?' Mike did not sound over-enthusiastic.

'I start work at nine tomorrow morning; until then, I'm free.' She smiled at Yuriko, and received a glowing smile in return. She would break her date – why not?

Mike looked from one face to another, recalling the day they had run towards him, the dark girl and the fair. Here they were, one on each side of him, smiling at each other. They hadn't smiled in the old days! 'Let's go,' he said. 'Curse having only one arm, I'm so proud of you both.'

'I have two,' said Mary. She stepped between them and linked together, they swung along the street. Mike hailed a taxi.

They entered a Japanese house, and sat in the room Mike had rented from a Japanese family. He paid for it with cigarettes and canned goods. Yuriko and Mike came to the house at all hours; no questions were asked, no greetings given them by Sudo San, their shamed and surly landlord.

Mary soon realised that Mike firmly intended to marry Yuriko Noguchi and she lingered on until she noticed Mike's interest in his wrist-watch.

'I must go, Mike, it is so late!'

'We'll find a taxi for you.' Mike spoke with alacrity. It was good and pleasant that Mary was back in his life again, but that didn't mean that she had to stay all night. He noticed a big change in her. Her beauty was at its peak, but the new brittleness in her would at times crack, and he could see the wistful Mary he had known in the house on the hilltop. At such times she had the look of a person who had lost something and was searching. 'We've told you all our news, all our problems, but you have told us so little about yourself,' said Mike.

'Yes, tell us about yourself,' Yuriko urged.

'Well,' Mary hesitated. 'I am worried about Suzuki San; I would like to know where and how she is.'

'Maybe I can find out for you about the old one,' said Yuriko helpfully.

'Thank you very much, Minnie Mouse.' Mike smiled at his girl.

'Don't mention it, Meeky San.' They laughed together, so intimately that Mary suddenly felt left out. 'Do you stay here together all night?' she asked, diffidently.

'On rare occasions, such as tonight. It's difficult for us. Yuriko's aunt is a dragon!'

'I see! Mike, can't you get married by a Shinto ceremony?'

'Yes, but it's not worth the paper it's written on. I must go home to the States, and then apply for a transfer back here to Japan. Sooner or later, permission will be given for marriages between American personnel and Japanese girls. We can wait if we have to.'

'Looks like we have to.' Yuriko was very sleepy, but feminine intuition, of which she had a rich supply, made her aware that Mary had come with them not only to give her friendship, but to obtain something from them, and was waiting for that something. Yuriko wished she knew what it was, for otherwise, it appeared, Mary intended to linger on.

'By the way, Mike,' said Mary casually, 'do you ever see Ludi Hoffer these days? Do you know where he lives?'

'I see him around sometimes; he's still a liaison officer with the Provost Corps; but do you mean to say that *you* never see him?'

'I never see him,' said Mary. 'Life in Tokyo is so crowded these days.'

They walked with her until they found a taxi. The taxi drove off with Mary, and, hand-in-hand, Mike and Yuriko returned to their room.

Mike lay on the floor-mattress, watching Yuriko disrobing. So childlike, and yet! That look he had just received over her satin shoulder as her blue silk kimono rippled like a wave on to the sand-coloured tatami. 'I love you,' he said, fervently.

Quicker than summer lightning, her expression changed to one of teasing unbelief. 'Me?'

'You.'

'Sure it is me?'

'Come here,' he commanded.

'Like this?' She threw him a shocked glance.

'Uh huh.'

Hastily she slipped into her pink-and-white striped sleeping-gown. 'I was with no clothes,' she reproached.

'I know, I have very good eyesight.'

'And you are very bad man – the worst man I know.'

'And *you* are showing off. Just how many men do you know?'

'Makimashita,' she said forlornly.

'That sounds like a very bad word – translate at once.'

Yuriko's fingers flew as she tied her sash. Eyes abrim with laugher, she explained. 'It means, I am defeated by your question, for I know only one man.'

'That's good,' he said contentedly.

She gathered up the discarded blue gown and folded it. 'I put on my sleep-gown for your pleasure, Mike.'

'I will have more pleasure in taking it off.'

'*That* is why I put it on.'

He lay in silence. Her husky soft voice flowed on. 'Mike, I wish that tonight would last for ever.' Her cool fingers traced his profile. 'Every night I am away from you I cry.'

'You shouldn't do that!'

'I cannot help it and, when I remember that you do not know that I am crying for you, I cry more than ever.'

'You shouldn't – you mustn't!' This girl filled his heart to breaking point. 'Come here, darling, come here. . . .'

When the dark head lay beside his, Mike also wished that this night, this moment, might indeed last for ever.

When morning arrived, rain and wind had taken charge of the weather in Tokyo, and Mike stood in the street watching her walk away from him to become just another Japanese girl in a crowded Japanese street.

'If I thought I would lose you, I would shoot myself,' he growled.

A stout Japanese housewife gave him a startled glance, and hastened on her way.

He could no longer see Yuriko. 'If I thought that I would ever lose her, I would cut my throat – but wide,' he growled again.

42

MARY and her escorting lieutenant sat together in the spacious lobby of the Imperial Hotel; music, talk and laughter flowed around them. 'I have decided to forgive you for ditching me last night,' he said.

'Thank you, kind sir.'

'You don't care a damn, do you, Mary?'

'Umm?' What had he said? She should at least listen to him; he was a pleasant, attentive young man.

'What's with you, Mary? Why do I spend so much time with you?'

'Huh?'

'You don't even hear what I'm saying!'

'I'm sorry, I was dreaming!'

'Shall we dance?' he urged. 'Let's go on from here to a night-club.' He was on his feet, holding out his hand – but Mary remained seated, for Ludi had just come through the hotel's revolving doors. He ran lightly up the shallow carpeted steps, and stood looking about him.

A girl with shining red hair, and a piquant laughing face, came up to him. He took her hand and tucked it under his arm. Talking and laughing animatedly, they came to take over the table that Mary and her lieutenant were so obviously about to vacate.

'Are we intruding?' asked Ludi, as he and the girl with red hair stood waiting. 'Tables are at a premium!'

'We're leaving,' the lieutenant said. 'We're on our way out. Come on, Mary!'

Ludi looked down, directly into Mary's eyes. 'Killed any policemen lately?' he asked lightly.

'Ludi!'

'What did you say? Did you say yes?'

With an effort she rose to her feet. 'No. I said No!'

'Well, I'm glad to hear that!' Giving full attention to his companion, he seated her with gallantry. The girl had a clear ringing voice. 'Did she really kill a policeman? Did she really, Ludi honey?'

'I don't know, never saw her before in my life.'

'Honey, you are just the craziest, but the craziest, man!'

Ludi spoke to the lieutenant. 'Thank you for letting us have your table.'

'We were going anyway,' said the lieutenant curtly. 'Come on, Mary.' He led her out through the revolving doors, and hailed a taxi. Mary, he thought, looked as though she were about to pass out. He hoped that he could off-load her before that happened.

What a date! Ditched last night – and now this.

The following morning Mary asked Amelia Francis if it would be possible to become a permanent staff member of the Red Cross and, if so, would it be possible to be transferred back to the States?

'I think it could be arranged.' Miss Francis looked keenly at her. There was trouble here, of that she was sure. 'Are you worried, Mary?'

'No, Miss Francis.'

'Homesick, perhaps?'

'Yes, homesick.'

'*That's* no good. I'll do all I can.'

'And could I leave soon, please, Miss Francis?'

'I'll try to arrange it, Mary. Confidentially, I'm leaving Japan myself, I really don't fit in here.'

'Neither do I.'

'I'll arrange for you to return to the States with me as soon as possible. I don't like Japan at all, and I think that this is no place for a nice girl like you. Too much excitement, too much pleasure, too many men, and too much false gaiety. Don't you agree, Mary?'

'Yes, I agree, Miss Francis.'

'Good, then that's settled. I'll arrange everything. You'll be glad to leave Japan, I *know*,' said Miss Francis, competently.

43

'LUDI,' said Stephen Barnes, 'there's someone here to see you.'

Looking up from his work, Ludi saw Mike Peters standing before his desk. 'Hi there, Mike! Long time no see.'

'Hi! Yes, I know. I've been busy and . . .'

'How come you two know each other?' interrupted Barnes.

'I read the newspapers,' said Ludi. 'I know about the adventures of Lieutenant Peters – who doesn't?'

Barnes looked at the two men curiously. 'I hear you're going home, Lieutenant?'

'Yes, day after tomorrow, Captain,' said Mike.

'Half your luck. Hoffer here is leaving us, too, and I'm going to miss Ludi Hoffer – don't know how I'm going to manage without the bastard.'

'Smile, when you call me that,' said Ludi.

'I'm smiling, man!' Barnes hesitated. 'I'll leave you to it, then.'

'Thanks! And don't slam the door.'

'My very funny friend!' said Barnes, as he slid the door smoothly shut. He really cared that Ludi would soon be leaving him; he had never had a more congenial side-kick.

'Ludi, you must help me,' demanded Mike.

'Again?'

'Please! I would like to get married before I leave for home, but it's impossible.' Mike sat down heavily.

'Married? Is that still on? I've seen your lady friend doing the town with a dozen different men. You must know that Mary leads a gay night life.'

'I never mentioned Mary.'

'No? I thought you had. Is it someone else, then? Let's get out of here; let's go to the park, the fresh air will clear my bewildered brain.'

They crossed the busy street. In the park the trees were bare; leaves carpeted the grass, and old Japanese gardeners speared them with pointed sticks.

'Now, begin at the beginning,' said Ludi. 'Tell me all.'

'It's a Japanese girl . . .'

Ludi interrupted. 'Mike, just a moment! I'm interested in your problems – couldn't be more so – but just look over there!'

Mike's gaze followed Ludi's pointing finger.

'That man sitting on the bench is old Noguchi! I'll swear he's sitting there still trying to ferret out why Captain Tanaka was killed. Mike! Come back!'

Mike had turned, and was walking, almost running, back along the path. Ludi gave chase. 'You fool, you're safe from him, he can't touch us. Tanaka's murder has been shelved, the Japs have many more important things on their minds these days than . . .'

Mike interrupted him. 'Noguchi has a daughter.'

'I know it, and a hot-eyed baby she is at that.'

'She is the girl – my girl, the girl I have been telling you about!'

'This is it!' said Ludi. 'My most dramatic moment. You want to marry Noguchi's daughter! If that isn't the Ace of Trumps, what is it? Does her father know?'

'He doesn't know!'

They walked on; Ludi placed his arm in the old familiar manner around his friend's shoulder. 'Go on with your story.'

'It's no story – it's true! I need your help. Promise you'll help me and Yuriko.'

'Yuriko, is that her name? Doesn't suit her; it means "lily" – but, of course, there are Tiger Lilies.'

'O.K., Ludi.' Mike's voice was despondent. 'So you're not interested.'

'Hold on. I'm going to do everything I can to further your plans. I once caught a quick glance of your "lily maid." Can't imagine a girl on earth I would rather see you tied to.'

'You mean it?'

'I mean it. She's hardy, daring. I'd say she has a lot of old Noguchi in her.'

'You couldn't possibly know so much about Yuriko all in one quick glance, and what did you mean – hot-eyed?' said Mike, indignantly.

'Hot – as in wonderful. I can tell a woman's character just by hearing the swish of her petticoat.'

'Are you never serious, Ludi?'

'Underneath always. Come on, Mickey, I'll fall in with any plan you have in mind – I mean it.'

They walked on. 'My worry,' said Mike, 'is that I'm ordered States Side, and I can't get permission to stay here any longer. I want to marry Yuriko, and take her with me, but that's not allowed. Now, I want some reliable person to keep an eye on her for me until I can get a chance to return here. Are you going to stay in Japan? If so, will you help me, Ludi – again?'

'I'll help you if I can, Mike – and yes, I'm staying in Japan. My baser instincts are aroused by the wide-open money-making possibilities that stare me in the face everywhere I look. In fact, I've bought a house for myself right here in Tokyo. It is big, beautiful – and mine. The first home of my own that I've ever had. You can't imagine, but I've spent my life in rooms.'

'Are you living there alone?'

'I thought you knew me better than that,' Ludi grinned.

44

Mr Noguchi had observed Ludi Hoffer walking towards him in the park. What manners foreigners had! Hoffer was actually pointing a finger at him, in all probability telling his companion a fantastic story of how he, Hoffer, had cleverly pulled the wool over his eyes. It did not matter now. The case of the Tanaka murder was officially shelved. The fact that no more inquiries were being made into such cases was all a part of the moral destruction of Japan, he mused. He had resigned from the police force on the grounds of ill-health, and he was glad that his resignation had been accepted.

He watched the two approaching men. Hoffer was more swashbuckling than ever. What power that American uniform had, in this occupied country of his! He agreed, in his mind, that this was surely the most benevolent Occupation in the history of mankind. Even the flag of Japan was once more, by courtesy – flying. But it was the small things, the undercurrents, of Occupation, that were so undermining, so hurtful.

A few days previously he had stood watching the white flag with its orange-red circle, had rejoiced to see it again, when – 'Man! Get an eyeful of that poached egg!' – two G.I.s had gone their way, laughing scornfully.

They had every right to their opinion. But now, all *he* saw when he looked at the flag was a poached egg. He had always disliked eggs cooked in such a manner, he preferred a well-cooked omelette.

Hoffer was drawing nearer. Would he stop and speak? Mr Noguchi hoped that he would. But no! He had turned, and was following the slender maimed young officer. They were actually – well, almost running.

Why? Mr Noguchi rose slowly to his feet. He spoke aloud as had always been his habit. 'I had rather thought that Hoffer would have enjoyed lording it over me. I am no good any more. I have lost my touch, all things now turn out contrary to my predictions.'

Weary, how weary life was. With his stick he poked at a decaying leaf that had fluttered tiredly down from its tree. 'Both of us, decayed and useless. I had better go home. Trouble enough there, too.'

Last night he had been shocked. His sister, a well-meaning woman, had merely announced that she had found a fine young man, a man suitable in every way for Yuriko to marry. What could be more normal?

Yuriko, his child, had protested hysterically.

'Enough!' He had spoken sternly, and she had gone resentfully to her room. An hour later she had reappeared, dressed in one of her best kimonos. Going out, always going out, restless – the new way. He didn't like it at all.

He would go home, talk with her, tell her – no need to marry this young man, but at least be courteous, you can meet him. He would chide her.

Passing a small park, he stood a moment and watched a rowdy group of American soldiers and Japanese girls – some surely not yet out of the schoolroom! He watched in awe as one man, picking up two girls, embraced them. He was, yes – kissing their mouths! The girls shrieked with excited laughter.

He hastened his steps. Home, decency, tea. He longed for a cup of fragrant tea.

> What though they conquer us?
> The tea has come.
> In at most nine hundred years,
> Someone will conquer them. . . .

The poem comforted him but little; it was difficult to take the long view.

Opening the gate of his brother-in-law's home, he faced his daughter. 'Going out again?' he asked gently.

'Yes, but not for long.'

Almost timidly, he caught at her kimono sleeve. 'Please! Come with me, I wish to speak with you.'

Impatiently she pulled the silk from his hand. 'I won't be long, Puppa.' How different from the little girl of long ago. Her hair was now swept back dramatically from a woman's brow, and – that look in her eyes!

He closed the gate. 'I wish to speak with you.'

Unwillingly she followed him into the house. They sat together on square silk floor-cushions. The tea in front of Mr Noguchi remained untasted. 'Now,' he said, 'in plain and simple words – tell me? Something is on your mind.'

'The truth is sometimes bitter,' she replied.

He liked the way she looked directly into his eyes. 'I know that even better than you. I have searched for truth all my life; it *is* often bitter.'

'I will never make an arranged marriage,' she murmured, and her voice was sulky.

He was relieved. 'There is no need for you to do so. You enter university next year – you will meet many young men.'

'I wish to marry for love.' She used the English word. These days she used so many, he had noticed this.

'Very commendable.'

'I think it is dreadful to marry a person you don't know – a stranger.'

'Your mother and I, our marriage was arranged for us, our wise parents arranged it.'

'A marriage with no love!' She put her face in her hands.

'No love! Your mother and I? No love?' He had never struck his child – but to speak like this! His hand moved, and he struck her. His lips were trembling; he covered them with his hand.

She leant over and, taking his other hand, held it between hers. 'Forgive me, Father. I knew you were happy – you and Mother. Please forgive me.'

'To think that I struck you!'

'It hurt me only because I caused you to do so.'

'Then – we forgive each other. I am weary. This is not the time for further talk.' He stood up.

'We *must* talk, Puppa.'

He sat down again, feeling most uneasy. She had such a look in her eyes. Her voice was like a water-wheel awhirl. What evil force had taken control of her? He listened in consternation as she spoke incoherently. To marry – love – so much, so hopelessly. Her many outings – the nights spent with her girl friend. Lies, all lies! With him – *him*. . . .

'Enough! Be quiet!' he whispered. Stretching across the table he caught her wrist in a vice-like hold. 'Take hold of yourself,' he ordered. 'Now! Who is this man?'

'You sent me to him – in the first place. . . .'

'I sent you to him? To whom?'

'You must remember! You sent me to the house on the mountain. The house of Mary Ogata.'

'Of what are you speaking?'

'It is he, the man from her house – it is he. . . .' Her voice trailed away.

A seething rage was born in his heart, but not against her. That arrogant, insolent, black-marketeer, murderer. That spoiler of womanhood. He groaned aloud. This man had taken his daughter – she was his prey.

He waited a moment. He could speak now. 'You are mistaken. The man you say cares for you, is bad. . . .'

'No.'

'You must believe me. I know him well. He is a man of low birth. Women are but a night's pleasure to him.'

'No!'

Now he knew why Hoffer had run from him today. Stolen fruit! His child, his precious child. 'You cannot care for this man.'

'I love him, he loves me.'

'You are bewitched.'

'If you say so, I am bewitched. But nothing shall come between us.'

'You can love a murderer? You shame me into speaking of things better not spoken of between father and daughter. This man, he was the lover of the woman in that house. With my own eyes I saw them naked in their bed together.'

'You lie.'

'I speak the truth.'

178

'I know you lie. Mike told me he has never seen you. That you have never seen him.'

'Who told you?'

'Mike – Michael Peters. He told me.'

'Even his name, the name he has used in your seduction, is false. His name is Hoffer – Ludi Hoffer.'

'Father – not that man!'

'Not – that man? There was no other man in that house.'

'Mike was there. Mr Hoffer found him, in the forest. Mike was wounded, ill. He had fallen from his bombing plane, from a B.29. Hoffer San brought him to the house on the mountain. The girl, Mary, she hid him there. All this, I heard from Mike. Many people know about Mike; the story was in many papers.' The pride in the young voice. 'Are you ill, Father?' She leant towards him in consternation.

So – that was it! So – it was like that? How blind he had been. How simple a case to solve. Fear of discovery! Frantic murder of Tanaka. . . . How clever they had been!

His daughter was speaking. He forced his attention back to her. 'Puppa, I must go. You say you know what it is to love. Let me go now. Mike and I have so little time.'

So! *That* was it! He had heard vaguely about an airman being hidden, but had not studied the newspapers lately. There was too much in them that was distressing to read.

'I am going.' She was on her feet. He caught at her flowing silken sleeve; not timidly, but demandingly, and with anger.

'You are not to go. I have suffered enough.'

She twirled skilfully out of his grasp. 'Enough? Always with you it is – enough. Me! I am just beginning.' In an impassioned voice she echoed, 'Beginning!'

She ran from the room. He heard her fumbling in the entrance as she slipped into her footwear, listened to the soft pad, pad of feet as she ran down the path. The gate slid open, then shut. She had gone.

Mr Noguchi sat by the low table. Tea! He picked up the bowl. It was cold, he had wanted hot tea. He placed it back on its lacquer stand.

45

MIKE and Yuriko had arranged to meet on the hilltop over-looking the Imperial Moat. This was a favourite meeting place for American soldiers and their Japanese girl friends. One could see them in couples at any time, beneath the willow trees, or leaning against the venerable pines, with long silences, happy laughter from the men, and giggles from the girls.

Mike and Yuriko often met there, but not to linger under the willows, waste time leaning against the trees. They would clasp hands, and walk away together swiftly; for they had a place of their own to go to.

Yuriko alighted from the bus. Mike would be waiting; she had never been late before. Even so, she walked slowly, deep in thought. Her father! always so good to her. How upset, puzzled he had been. His life had been so swiftly wrecked – his wife dead, and now his daughter behaving so badly. Tears blinded her.

She raised her eyes to the hilltop. Mike! There he was, he had seen her, was coming to meet her. In a few days he would be gone, ordered home. How dreadful it would be for him, if their love was *not* good for him.

He was walking briskly on the other side of the road. Her eyes were misty as she darted across the street.

An army truck was travelling swiftly. The G.I. was a fine driver, but he had no chance. It was as though a butterfly had fluttered across the road.

The truck's brakes screamed as he pulled up twenty yards down the hill. He ran back as quickly as his trembling legs would carry him. The girl lay there, so very still. The wheels had gone over her – such a heavy truck, such a fragile girl! The sleeves of her gay kimono were spread out on the dusty road like the wings of a crushed butterfly.

'Jesus!' the truck-driver groaned.

He saw that a young lieutenant, an empty sleeve pinned

neatly against his shoulder, was kneeling alongside the crushed body, gently straightening the torn clothes. He lifted a sleeve of the kimono, and with it covered her face. He remained kneeling there, protectively, his hand holding one of her hands, dazed incredulity in his eyes.

A curious crowd gathered; an ambulance arrived, and M.P.s in a jeep. The American lieutenant climbed into the ambulance too. Its siren faded into the distance, wailing, and the truck-driver crossed himself hastily. The M.P.s hustled him to his truck.

'What happened?' they asked briskly.

'She gave me no chance to pull up. . . . She stepped out from the sidewalk in front of my wheels, without looking to the right or to the left . . . Jesus! I'll never forget it.'

46

LUDI sat in the hotel bedroom with Mike, and wished that someone else was doing this job. There had been a phone call to him from the hospital to come and fetch Mike, who had asked for him. 'Don't let him out of your sight,' a doctor there had said.

'What's happened?'

'He saw his Japanese girl friend run over by a truck and killed. He came with the body here in the ambulance. He's badly shocked. Take him to his quarters and stay with him. He's Lieutenant Peters, the man who fell. . . . '

'I know,' said Ludi. 'I'll attend to him.'

'Thanks. He's not our responsibility.'

Now Ludi was feeling that this situation was more than he could manage. He could not sit calmly by and watch a fellow human suffer, and Mike, poor cuss, was suffering, was a mess. What did one do with a man who raved continuously, against the world, himself – everything? It was hard to take, but not as hard as watching the deadly calm and realisation that came so suddenly, when Mike, looking at him in bewilderment, speaking in bewilderment, said, 'Ludi, she can't be dead. She was running to meet me. She can't be dead.'

How grand it would have been to answer, 'That's right! She's not dead.' But she was dead, and Ludi said flatly, 'Yuriko is dead, Mike.'

'Then – this is for real?'

'For real.'

Mike's face crumpled like the face of an unfairly punished child. Ludi recalled the vivacious Japanese girl, the innocent flirtatious glance she had once thrown in his direction. It was not his prerogative to stop Mike's despair. He settled down to wait, but when an hour had passed by he began to feel differently. This couldn't go on indefinitely! Going to the bed, he touched Mike's shoulder.

He'd done the wrong thing; the raving started again. Eyes swollen and slitted with misery, Mike yelled, 'Take your ugly face out of my sight!'

Ludi went out of the room. Women were better at doing this kind of thing than men were. He would call Mary: let her take over. Maybe it was the wrong thing to do, but it was better than doing nothing. At the end of the corridor was the telephone; someone was using it; he waited impatiently.

Mary was doing a rush job when her phone rang. She spoke abruptly into the mouthpiece. 'Yes?'

'Mary?'

In a parched desert, rain had come and suddenly the desert was aglow with colour.

'Ludi!' she whispered.

'Are you there?' he asked impatiently.

'Yes.'

'I can hardly hear you. Something must be wrong with the line.'

'Is this better?' She spoke loudly.

182

'Don't shout like that. Have you heard about Noguchi's daughter?'

'Noguchi's daughter?'

'That's right. You know that Mike has been seeing her?'

'Yes.'

'Have you heard about the accident?' he asked.

'What accident? What do you mean?'

His voice sounded weary. 'She was knocked down by an army truck.'

'No. Oh, no. . . .'

'She's dead, Mary.'

The desert was parched again. It would take something like this to make Ludi call her. 'Where is Mike?' she asked.

'With me. That's why I'm calling you. Will you come to him? I think you should.'

'Just tell me where – I'll come at once.'

'That's good,' said Ludi, and he gave her directions. 'I'll be seeing you, then.' The phone went dead.

Slinging a coat about her shoulders, she caught up her bag.

'Where, if I may ask, do you think you are going?' asked one of her co-workers. 'You can't just walk out like this – this is a priority job; the old girl will give birth to a foal.'

'Let her.' Mary hurried out into the grey rain of Tokyo's late afternoon.

Ludi was waiting for her in the corridor outside Mike's room. Breathless from her run up the stairs, she stood looking at him, uncertainly.

'You took your time getting here,' he said.

She shook her head as though to clear it. 'I came as quickly as I could.' She took a deep breath. 'Where is Mike now?'

'In there. Mary, I don't think you've understood how seriously shocked he is.'

'I think I understand. Shall I go in alone?'

'Yes, I can do nothing.' But when she opened the door he followed.

Her mind had been mainly on her meeting with Ludi, but,

as she looked down at Mike, all thought of herself, of Ludi, faded away. Sitting on the bed, she cradled his head against her bosom. 'Mike, it's dreadful. It can't be true. . . .'

Ludi watched, as Mike held on to her in desperation. 'Mary, what am I going to do? I loved her so – more than life.'

'I know.' She also began to weep. 'More than life – oh, darling, I know.'

After a while Mike sat up, and looked about him with rational eyes. 'Don't cry any more, Mary – thank you for crying, but don't cry any more.'

But Mary, it seemed, couldn't stop crying to order, and Mike, distressed by her tears, became aware that they were not alone. 'Don't just stand there, Ludi! Get Mary a drink.'

Ludi poured the drinks with a trembling hand; he felt like bawling himself. How wonderful to cry, get relief from pent-up feelings. He hadn't cried since childhood.

Mike downed the brandy at one gulp. 'Look after her, Ludi, I'm going to take a hot shower.' He hurried into the bathroom, and soon the subdued sound of running water came from behind the closed door.

47

THEY sat in silence, Ludi longing to be out of this cage of misery. It seemed to him that Mike was taking a very long shower – reluctant no doubt to leave the curtain of warmth and anonymity found in a bathroom, and to come out into the world of cold truth.

Standing by the window, Ludi spoke casually to Mary. 'It's raining again. I thought maybe it would snow.'

How impersonal, untouchable, he was. 'It's much too cold for snow,' she murmured, and wondered what would he do if she did as she longed to do, put her arms about him. As she stepped across the room, he turned, and she saw the familiar movement of his hand passing over his face.

'I don't know how to deal with Mike! Mary, can you stay? I mean – all night?'

'I can stay.'

'You had better call your headquarters.'

'No need for that.'

'Well, I suppose you know.'

'Know what?' she asked lightly.

As lightly, he replied, 'Occupation-girls are said to spend quite a few nights out all night and no questions asked.'

'That's not true! The rules are very strict, most of the girls are fine girls and,' she continued stiffly, 'I'm no Occupation-girl!' There! he was making her angry again.

'No? I've heard a different story.'

'The conventions are, as I said, very strict.'

Ludi laughed. 'Well, conventions have never worried you, Madame Ogata.'

If he still enjoyed hurting her, did he really despise her so much? She had to find out. 'Ludi, do you hate me?'

'Mary, I once thought you to be the darlingest of girls.'

'And now?' she asked courageously.

He smiled directly into her eyes. 'And now – I don't! Sure you wouldn't like another drink?'

She had left herself open to that sharp thrust. 'Yes,' she replied, 'I'd like a drink, and I think we should order up some food for Mike. Don't you think it's time he came out of the shower?'

'No, it won't hurt him.' It would be a good idea if the poor guy drowned himself, went down the drain. 'You're right about ordering up food for him; order some for yourself, too.'

'And for you?'

'Not for me, I'm clearing out, I'll be here again in the morning. I don't want to see Mike again tonight, I can't comfort him. That's one reason that makes me want to go, but the other is that I thought seeing you wouldn't hurt. It does. Don't look so happy. It hurts because I don't like being so close to a woman who looks as though butter wouldn't melt in her mouth, but has the sting of an asp in that very same mouth – so I'm going!'

Ludi went down to the lobby, and out into the windy wet Tokyo night. A taxi pulled up. 'You want taxi?' The driver's head was covered with long black bristles. Probably a returned soldier growing his shaven hair.

'Yes. Take me down-town.'

'Hai hai. Yes, take you anywhere.'

Ludi climbed in. 'Were you a soldier?' he asked.

'No.'

'What did you do during the war?'

'Why do you ask? Is anything wrong?'

'No,' said Ludi. 'I was wondering why you had shaved your hair, and why you are letting it grow.'

'Aaah!' The man laughed. 'During the war, as now, I drove a taxi. During the war, it was patriotic and smart to shave my head.'

'And now?'

The driver laughed again. 'And now – it is smart to let my hair grow.'

'What about the patriotic question?'

'Oh, that!' said the man, and Ludi hung on to the rail of the front seat as the cab slewed dangerously under acceleration. 'I copy Democlatic way – it is new.'

'I like the old ways better,' said Ludi.

The taxi slowed down to a crawl. The man craned his head to look at his passenger. 'You do?' he asked incredulously.

'Yes, and take me for a drive around town for half an hour, then back to the hotel.'

They drove on through the crowded streets, and the cab driver shook his head in puzzlement, as only a Japanese can.

Ludi re-entered the hotel, and went up to Mike's room. It had occurred to him that Mike might have started raving again, and that it would be too much for Mary to manage. Anyway, he had returned – no matter why.

There was no answer to his knock. He tried the handle, the

door opened – an empty room. He went downstairs. 'Has Lieutenant Peters gone out?' he inquired at the desk.

'Yes, sir.'

'Was he alone?'

'No, sir, a young lady . . .'

Ludi took a seat in the lobby. Life, busy and gay, moved around and past him. He closed his eyes.

An hour later, Mary and Mike walked in and through the lobby. Hand-in-hand, across the thick carpet up the stairs, they went. They did not notice him. Mike was pale, but seemed calmer now.

Beckoning to the white-coated boy-san, Ludi ordered, 'Bring me a whisky.' Quite plain to see he wasn't needed.

48

MIKE was waiting at the airport for the call to passengers to go on board the aircraft. The wind was cold; he shivered, and looked at his two friends. There was an empty space in him – no force. It was difficult to speak, but there was something he meant to ask them to do for him.

Mary's gloved hand tightened about his; her hand had hardly been out of his for the last many heavy hours. Last night, she had, without asking where, gone with him, and had stood outside the small Buddhist cemetery, in the rain, for at least half an hour, while he went in alone.

There, on a bright day, he had been before. There he had held Yuriko for the first time.

Now, at the airport, he had something to ask, knowing that Mary and Ludi would not refuse. 'Will you go tomorrow' – his voice dropped to a whisper – 'to the funeral . . .'

'We'll be there, Mike,' said Ludi. 'I was going to speak to you about it.'

'And afterwards, Mary – you know the room, where you visited us? There's something I want from there.'

He cleared his throat; he had intended to speak casually, rather gruffly, but his voice was thin. 'I want something sent to my home address in the States. I've written what I want – here!' From his pocket he took a small slip of paper. 'I don't want any stranger seeing or touching . . .'

'O.K., then,' said Ludi, 'we'll do as you ask. It's time to go.' Ludi placed his arm for the last time around Mike's shoulder. 'Let's make this quick – Sayonara, Mike!' He turned and walked briskly away.

Mike kissed Mary, and picking up his bag walked towards the waiting aircraft.

On the trip back to the city in a taxi, Mary sat quietly beside Ludi. Several times he glanced at her, but her eyes were closed. He wondered if she had fallen asleep, overcome by the exhaustion of her night-long watch at Mike's side.

Now Mike's request meant that he and Mary would have to meet again tomorrow. He would have to make arrangements for that. 'Mary,' he said, quietly. She opened her eyes and then closed them again. So, she didn't want to talk? Well, neither did he. They drove on in silence to the Red Cross Headquarters.

'I leave you here,' he said. 'Listen, Mary, I'll have a little trouble in finding out about the funeral tomorrow . . .'

She stood beside him on the pavement. 'You'll manage.' Her voice sounded weary, uninterested.

'And do you have any idea how we can find that house where Mike and his girl had their room?'

'I know where the place is.'

'Do you have to speak like a dead woman? I know you're tired, but can't you show a little pep?'

'No.'

'Right! Selfish to the last. I'm tired, too.' He was, he had never felt so emotionally worn out. 'There's something else I want to ask you.'

'Yes?'

'About Suzuki San, have you ever contacted her? She was damn good to you.'

'Suzuki San was *wonderfully* good to me.'

'Then don't you feel indebted to her?'

'I am, as you say selfish; no, I don't feel indebted to her.'

'If you'd care to see her, that's her address.' He gave her a card. She took it without looking at it, and put it in her pocket. 'Do you see her?' she asked in surprise.

'I do, I like to keep my friends.'

She watched him drive away. She would like to see Suzuki San again. But – no. Whatever had been was finished, and done with.

49

ARRIVING home from his daughter's funeral, Mr Noguchi knew that he must at once seek solitude, be alone with the turbulent sorrow that was fermenting within him.

At the entrance stood his old cousin, shoulders bent with age, her sparse hair pinned in a hard little knob. She had been in the world for eighty-seven years, and enjoyed each one of them. Every funeral she attended was a triumph. She appeared as jolly and gay as though on a cherry-blossom viewing party. Holding a bowl of coarse-grained salt, she energetically threw it on the shoulders of those returning from the funeral. Everyone knew that salt had the power to scare bad spirits away. 'Choto!' she admonished her kinsman. 'Come back! You got no salt.' Mr Noguchi received a sprinkling of crystal on his black-coated shoulder.

He had always been an admirer of restraint, a past-master at it, but this swelling grief refused to remain restrained. His sister and others present watched him with embarrassment as he entered the house, walked along the gleaming corridor, and disappeared into his daughter's room.

Only the old salt-thrower remained at ease. Surely it was time for refreshment! There should always be a feast after a wedding or funeral. 'I should think it was about time for refreshment – something hot, yes, and sweet!' she reminded the mourners. The atmosphere grew easier. Trust an old one to relieve tension.

Noguchi remained alone in Yuriko's room. As he wept, his head moved from side to side as though denying the reason for his grief. There, surrounded by the inanimate possessions of his child, the realisation that she was never to be seen, heard or touched again, became solid fact.

When the house grew silent, and lights from the street-lamps made ghostly shadows on the tatami, he left the room, bathed, and changed into a dark grey kimono. His wife had chosen the heavy raw silk, sewn every stitch in it. Returning to Yuriko's room, he decided to spend the rest of the night there, sorrowing, remembering, measuring his guilt.

When the new day arrived, he would know if he were able to stay in the everyday world of living. It was necessary now to consider the situation calmly, to review all the circumstances logically, clearly, and to find an answer to the question: Why had his only child gone from life so suddenly? Her mind had always been like a clear rushing stream, with unexpected depths. He had delighted in her capacity for deep thought. Her childhood years had been a joy to him. War had come – years of unnatural strain. The war had ended. Older people such as he had become preoccupied with the problems of defeat, of being an occupied country. They had forgotten the awakening desires, longings, of the sons and daughters in their care.

He had not noticed that the eyes of his daughter were now those of a woman. Mourning for his wife, suffering frustration from his failure to unravel the Tanaka case, he had spent his days, sleepless nights, pandering to sorrow, to conceit.

When Yuriko, in that new self-assured voice, had told him, 'I love a man,' it had been a severe blow to his pride, but when he had realised that the man was an American . . . *that* American . . .

Had he then given his daughter the courtesy that he had brought her up to expect from her father? Had he been tender, taken time to look into the hot young heart? Had he been calm, a comforting, understanding father?

Remembering his behaviour, he could not endure himself.

No use to cry out in torment; useless to think how it could have been. Had his harshness, in fact, driven her to her death?

From babyhood, she had been fed on admiration for those who took their lives. The traditional Japanese readiness to pay the last sacrifice of obedience would have seeped into her mind unconsciously. He, himself, had told her tales of proud young people who had committed *hara-kiri*.

She had read a thousand poems extolling the virtues of a self-taken life. What, then, had been in her mind when she had stepped in front of a speeding vehicle?

In her irrational mood, had a moment of melancholy, a hopelessness for the outcome of her romance taken possession of her?

He could not bring himself to think that Yuriko, clear thinking, sensible girl, had carelessly allowed a truck to knock her down. It was so entirely out of keeping with her character.

Had it been an accident? His punishment was a heavy one. He would never really know.

50

LUDI and Mary had attended the Buddhist funeral service, and as the cumbersome dark red hearse made its way along the narrow street and disappeared, Ludi replaced his hat and turned to Mary. 'I've caught a cold in that dismal hall.' He blew his nose.

'Everyone should cry at a funeral. It's the thing to do,' murmured Mary.

'Crying – me? Well, I always like to do the right thing.' He changed the subject. 'Noguchi looked a sick man.'

'He made me think of his country's emblem – a once crisp, bold chrysanthemum that has weathered a storm and is now frayed, withered and old!'

'You are wrong,' said Ludi. 'The chrysanthemum is not the right emblem for this country. You are mistaken.'

'Me, and about ninety million others.'

'If you and ninety million others compare a withered flower with Japan, you are all wrong! People like Suzuki San are more typical of Japan. Sturdy bamboo! A typhoon lays bamboo flat, but, when the storm's over, it stands up, resilient, tenacious, pushing up new shoots.'

She looked at him in indignation. 'I've heard you say a dozen times that you dislike Japan!'

'*Touché!* And so I have, but that was war talk and even I can be mistaken. I like Japan, I like the people; I'm going to make my life here.'

'I hope you'll be very happy. It would be rather nice if you had a little tracery of bamboo on your business cards.'

He smiled. 'That's a good idea – but if I don't have a drink soon, I'll blow my top. Do you mind if we have lunch before we go on to do that other job that Mike asked us to do?'

'I don't mind.'

They sat at a table for two. She picked at the food in front of her; Ludi ate ravenously. 'Funerals always make me hungry,' he explained.

A girl with a shining head of red hair crossed the crowded grill-room and stood behind Ludi, covering his eyes with her hands. 'Guess who?' she asked.

'Guess nothing! I paid for that perfume.' He rose to his feet, and stood looking down at her. 'I deserve everything you're going to say. I've neglected you wickedly – all that and more.' He grinned confidently. 'You forgive me?'

'I'm not sure.' She looked at Mary. 'Ludi, you told me that you had never seen this person before, and here you are practically holding hands over lunch.'

'Mrs Ogata and I – Mary, this is Debby Lawson – Mrs Ogata and I have been to the funeral of a friend; I don't want to talk about it. Do you mind, Deb?'

'About the funeral, I don't mind; but I can't imagine why you told me that you did not know Mrs Ogata. That's a Jap name, isn't it?'

'Czechoslovakian.' Ludi grinned again.

'It's Japanese,' said Mary.

'I've never seen a blonde Japanese.'

'Then this must be an interesting experience for you,' answered Mary, wearily.

'Mary's an American,' said Ludi. 'I'll see you tonight. Be a honey, Debby – scram!'

'I don't want to wait until tonight, I want to talk to you now, please, Ludi.'

He hesitated. 'Do you mind, Mary? Do you mind sitting alone for a while?'

'I don't mind in the least.'

The hotel grill-room was crowded, noisy. She sat looking at the white tablecloth until he rejoined her. 'Where's this place that we're going to?' he asked.

'We'll go there in a taxi. The house is owned by a Japanese family named Sudo,' she replied, and she was amazed at the steadiness in her own voice.

51

THE room she stood in was where Mary had witnessed and envied the joyous, frankly amorous behaviour of Mike and Yuriko. There, on the tatami, were the two bright-red floor cushions. There, side by side, were the two sleep-mats. Instead of folding them with usual Japanese neatness, Yuriko had lazily left them ready to be used. But the flowers, that Yuriko had so carefully arranged in the Tokonoma alcove, were dead.

Ludi looked about him. So this was the setting for Mike's grand passion! This very ordinary Japanese room. He regretted coming here. Somehow, the cheap room, the moral indignation and shame of the house-owner who had unwillingly allowed them entry, brought the love of Mike and Yuriko Noguchi down to the level of an *affaire.*

'The flowers have died,' said Mary.

Ludi looked at the wilted flowers. 'Symbolical! Let's do what we have to do, and get out of here.' He opened the cupboard door, and found two small travelling bags. 'You pack the girl's things. I'll take care of Mike's.' From his pocket-book he took Mike's scrap of paper. 'There's a floor-lamp somewhere.' He switched it on and the veiled light of the thick paper lampshade cast a delicate spell over the room. Perhaps it was not such a bad place after all.

He held Mike's scrap of paper to the light, and was silent for a moment. 'All he wants,' said Ludi impatiently, 'is – a pink-and-white striped kimono!'

As she went on with her packing, he gathered up the few male possessions which lay about the room. 'Have you nearly finished, Mary? Let's get out of here, as quickly as possible.'

'Do you have to be quite so callous about everything?'

'I'm not being callous; it's just that I have other things to do.'

'I, also, have things to do.' She spoke quietly. 'I have my own packing; many ends to tie up before I leave on Saturday. But Mike asked us to do this small thing for him. You could show a little more grace.'

'Where are you off to?'

'I'm going to Red Cross H.Q. in New York – a permanent billet there. My boss, Miss Francis, arranged it for me.'

'Why didn't you tell me?'

'Because I knew that you wouldn't be interested!' She stood up. 'Well! I've packed everything, but I can't find the pink kimono.' Her eyes searched the room. Peeping from beneath a pillow on one of the sleep-mats was a cloud of pink. 'There it is!' She pointed.

Ludi picked up the kimono, held it in his strong brown hands and felt a wave of regretful tenderness towards the young Japanese girl. 'It was the gown she slept in.' He handed the kimono to Mary. 'Poor Yuriko,' he said, 'it's the saddest story.'

'Not as sad as mine.' She crushed the pink-and-white garment against her breast. 'Don't send me away from you, Ludi!' she cried. 'You did love me – once. Can't you love me again? Were those dreadful words I said to you so completely beyond forgiveness? Don't send me away!'

He looked at her in astonishment. 'Who's sending you away?'

'You are!' she whispered, and began to cry, as she had never cried before.

He made no move to comfort her, and when he spoke his voice was harsh. 'Don't cry, Mary. You know that I despise tears – tears of self-pity, that is.'

'But *will* you forgive me?'

'Don't let's talk about it, what's past is past. Instead, I want to tell you something about myself, something I would like you to know. Do you want to hear it? I once told you about my mother. . . .'

'If only you hadn't,' she whispered.

'*I'm* very glad that I did, but that was only a part of my story, because somewhere, perhaps long ago, I know that I had a very proud ancestor, for all my life I have felt that I am a naturally decent person.'

'You are, you are!' she cried passionately.

'Well! How about that!' He grinned at her. 'Now! From the time I grew up I began to dream a very special dream. Some day, I have always known, it will not be a dream. My dream never varies. I'm an elderly man, standing in a crowded place and I

195

am filled with contentment and happiness. In my dream, I can't understand why I feel that way, until, through the crowd, a woman walks towards me. Then I know! She is my wife, and she accepts me as I am; loves me because of what I am. I've never seen her face in my dreams. Once, for a short time, I truly thought I'd found her – in real life.' He was silent.

'Ludi,' she began. She must let him know that she loved him, accepted him.

He patted her shoulder. 'We won't talk about it any more – I just wanted to let you know how I feel about certain events in our past.'

'But,' interrupted Mary stubbornly, 'if you are as decent, as fine as you think, then you should be big enough to forgive what I said when I was mad with you. I want you to know that I *do* understand. That I also crave contentment, happiness. I . . .'

Now he patted her hand. 'I hope that you will find happiness somewhere, with someone, Mary – just as long as it isn't with me. Now! shall we make tracks?'

She spoke slowly. 'I could forgive you anything. No matter what you said to me, did to me . . .'

'Talk is easy.' He made a package of the pink kimono. 'Will you take this to New York, or what shall we do with it?'

'You don't know the meaning of love; you don't know yourself at all,' she continued. 'You are so wrapped up in your tragic youth, your pathetic childhood . . .'

'What shall we do with Yuriko's other things?' he interrupted impatiently.

'I shall send them to Mr Noguchi – he loved his daughter. And Ludi! About that mother of yours! Are you so proud and decent that you've never heard the story of Mary Magdalene? Are you so almighty that no one who injures you can be forgiven?' Her voice flared into anger. 'Whatever my faults may be, I now think that I have taken more than my share of punishment and insults. If you're sorry for some things you've done in life, so am I. Now, that should make us even. I wish you everything that you wish for yourself, and I'm *sure* that you will have what you wish, for I've never known a more conceited, selfish, human being.'

'You,' Ludi interrupted acidly, 'have the makings of a *fine* Women's Organisation worker. I can see you, ten years from now, using hairpins, and disillusioned, and bitter, and bad-tempered. No one who knows you then will imagine that you have committed, or helped to commit, murder, married an Oriental, or that you were once an ardent, passionate girl.'

'I'm listening,' she said.

'Well, listen some more,' he continued, slowly. 'I had no idea that you had it in you to sound off as you did when you said that my mother was not so bad; and yes, I do know the story of Magdalene – who better? I know the cast-out-malice teachings of Buddha, and the Shinto doctrine that the fortunes of the living depend upon the well-being of the dead. All these things – I know . . .'

'That last one must really knock you at times,' interrupted Mary. 'I can already see you setting up a Kamidana, a neat little Shinto God-shelf, and mumbling prayers to the revered spirit of the mother you have slang-banged all these years. I see you trotting to the seashore, a little straw boat clutched in your hand, a straw boat laden with food, and messages of love to Mother. I see you doing this at the Festival of the Dead, not leaving anything to chance that could stand in your way to success, to good fortune.' She ceased speaking, and glared at him.

He laughed cynically. 'I had never thought of doing that! It's a wonderful idea, I'll buy a Kamidana tomorrow; everyone should have one, and I'll think deeply about the little straw boats. As you so wisely say, why leave anything to chance?' He tossed the packaged kimono at her feet. 'A woman with so much fire and energy can easily finish off this little job alone. I'll send a cab to pick you up.'

'Don't bother! And you just go on dreaming your dreams – you'll need them, when you're an old man.'

She spoke to an empty room, and Mr Sudo put his gloomy face around the door. 'You are leaving?' he asked.

'Yes.'

'Do you know what became of the young Japanese woman who used to come here?'

'She was killed,' said Mary bitterly.

'Not killed by . . .?'

'By a *truck*,' said Mary. 'Not by the man who loved her.'

Ludi had sent a cab. Mr Sudo willingly carried the cases out, and dumped them into the back seat. He slammed the cab door and walked back to his house.

52

SNUGGLING beneath warm bedclothes, Mary wondered what to do with the hours ahead. This evening she would be winging her way to New York! Springing from bed, she shrugged into a robe and joined the queue of women waiting for showers.

'How's a girl, Mary? Haven't seen you around.'

'I've been around.'

'Are you glad to go, Mary? Or are you sorry to leave this Oriental madhouse?'

'That, my friends,' said Mary, 'will remain my secret.'

'Another secret? Your life appears to be a mass of such-like.'

'No.'

'But, yes. I saw you lunching with Ludi Hoffer. Now I, personally, and many of my sex, some a-standin' right here in this Lonely Hearts queue, have at some time or other fallen flat on our faces to have him take notice – to no avail. How come you know him?'

'He is a friend of the American lieutenant – the one whose Japanese girl was killed by a truck.'

'And so?'

'I also know the American lieutenant whose Japanese girl was killed by a truck. That's all. We attended the girl's funeral together.'

'Honey, don't tell me! Do Japanese have funerals? I never think of them as real people. . . .'

'They have funerals. Yuriko Noguchi was a real and lovely girl.'

'Don't get mad, honey. I was only kidding.'

'It's a nasty habit, kidding. You should try and break yourself of it.' Then Mary smiled at the girl. 'Sorry, I'm a bit off this morning.'

There was something she could do. She could take Yuriko's clothing to Mr Noguchi. She hoped that he would understand her reason for going to his house, but with Japanese people one never knew.

Mike had pointed out to her the Noguchi home. It was near the Buddhist cemetery. She found her way there and knocked at the door. Nervously, she told the surprised maid that she had called to see Noguchi Sama.

'Ah! So-desuka? Is that so?' The girl disappeared, and by her expression Mary knew that she had been wrong in coming to a house of such recent bereavement. But perhaps Mr Noguchi would understand that her visit at that time was unavoidable. She would have to explain that, and apologise for intruding.

An immaculate Mr Noguchi sat at his desk, making plans for his future, but no matter how he ordered his mind away from facts, every moment or so his heart would swell with grief. Time, he needed time.

Perhaps the new profession he had decided to enter would help. He had made up his mind to become a theatre critic. He had many friends in the literary world, and he had confidence that he would be a success. Not that it mattered – but, as well to be a success as a failure. . . . He would call one of his influential friend now.

199

He was annoyed when the servant announced a visitor. It must be a person of no sensitivity. 'Show the guest into the sitting-room,' he said, and looked inquiringly over the rim of his spectacles, for the servant was lingering on.

'It is a woman.' She answered his unspoken question. 'A young foreign woman, in the uniform of the Red Cross. She has your daughter's case with her. She speaks Japanese.'

So! Mr Noguchi thought. It could be none other than Mary Ogata. He had seen her at the funeral with Hoffer, both in their American uniforms. Apparently they knew of the love-affair of his daughter and the airman. They had known, or certainly Mary Ogata had known, of this love-affair which could only have begun in her house.

He sat deep in thought. In the workings of fate, his daughter's death had been a sequel to his assignment to the Tanaka case. He wished no publicity, none whatever, to be given to the circumstances that had led him to send his starving child to that cottage of mystery among the pinewoods on the hill.

He had never been an intimidator – rather, an inveigler, one who had used atmosphere, words, as his tools. Words, he had often proved, could cause imperspicuity, cause a mind to lose its brightness; words could cast a spell. He wanted to know the details of Tanaka's murder, for his own satisfaction only, for conceit, he admitted. Could he, with his long experience of the magic, mesmeric use of words, fling a gossamer black veil and cloud this woman's mind to get the facts from her? He could at least try. Put his own mind at rest – start off anew in life without this nagging sense of failure.

But no! That part of him was dead – let it remain dead.

He sighed. The maidservant was looking at him curiously. 'Tell the foreign woman,' he said, 'that I am not at home. If she gives you my daughter's case, take it to my sister.'

As the servant went out of the room, Noguchi said quietly to himself, 'Enough! I want no more of it.' He would telephone to his friend, a man of intellect, influence, who would use that influence as a start on his new way of life. He picked up the telephone.

Aaah! There was his friend's voice now, the voice of an impatient man. If he did not answer at once, the phone would be slammed down.

Noguchi was unable to speak, his heart was aching, his throat aching again, unbearably. His entire future lay in his ability to use his voice before the phone went dead in his hand.

He had had enough of dead things, of death. 'Noguchi speaking,' he said, and his voice was calm, controlled.

53

MARY accepted the snub from Mr Noguchi as natural enough in the circumstances. She gave Yuriko's bag to the maidservant, and then wandered aimlessly to the shopping district of the Ginza.

This was her last day in Japan and she wished, now, that she could find Suzuki San, say good-bye to her. Where was that card with her address, that Ludi had given her? She felt in the tunic pocket. Not there! She had mislaid it somewhere; perhaps in the tunic of her other uniform that was already packed. Well! It didn't matter, not really. She checked in at the desk at Red Cross H.Q., picked up her key, and was halfway to the elevator before the boy-san called to her.

'What is it?' she asked, impatiently.

'Person has been here asking for you.'

'For me?'

'Hai, yes. Waited many hours – for you.'

'Did he leave a message?'

'Yes. No.'

'No message?'

'Yes, left message. No, not he – old Japanese woman left message for you.'

'Suzuki San!' It could only be Suzuki San – not Ludi. Her disappointment was overwhelming.

'Hai – yes, Suzuki San.' The clerk was delighted with her cleverness.

'May I have the message?'

'Only o'denwa, num-bum, telephone number. Here it is. Old woman say – you be sure to call her. She wants to see you, but she is old and does not want to come back here. You, the old woman said, are not old, so you best go to her.' He laughed. 'Very nice old Japanese lady, yes?'

'Very nice,' agreed Mary. 'Will you put that call through for me, here?'

She held the receiver to her ear. Her throat tightened; how good to hear that crackling, vibrant old voice again! 'Suzuki San?'

'So – desu, Suzuki.'

'Suzuki San – it is Mary.'

'Hai – yes.'

How abrupt she sounded. 'Suzuki San, you came to my place today?'

'Hai – yes.'

'You asked me to call you on the telephone, to come and see you?'

'Hai – yes.'

'Suzuki San, you sound upset. Are you upset?'

'Hai – yes.'

'Why?'

'Suzuki don't like telephone.'

Mary smiled. 'Suzuki San, give me your address. I'll write it down now.'

'What? What are you saying, Mary Sama?'

Could it be that Suzuki San was forgetting her English? 'Are you working for a Japanese family now?' Mary asked.

There was a long silence, and when she spoke Suzuki's voice was exasperated. 'Mary Sama,' she said slowly and loudly, 'I work for Ludi Sama. You know that!'

As once before, the parched desert of Mary's future burst into flower. 'Did he send you to me?'

'Sure! Why not! He wants to *see* you, Mary Sama. Why not?'

Why not indeed! Mary listened as Suzuki's crackling voice continued, 'So you come? Not far. Only in Koji-machi.' She added the number of street and house. 'You come, Mary Sama?'

'Yes,' said Mary, 'I'll come at once,' and she thought; if I had wings, I would *fly*.

As her taxi drove through Koji-machi, one of the finest residential quarters in Tokyo city, Mary noticed that here very little damage had been caused by fire and bomb. The streets were lined with strong high walls, protecting and hiding from sight the homes behind them.

The taxi driver pulled up with a screeching of brakes. 'This is the house you asked for,' he declared.

Opening a heavy wooden gate, she stepped into a garden that was a wonderland of Japanese magic. Softly falling snow was outlining every small twig on every tree and shrub; the rims of lily ponds glistened with an encrusted sparkle, laid there by the snow.

Enchanted, she gazed at the flawless beauty and quietude surrounding her. A small garden, but surely that grove of bamboos to the right was part of a large forest! It could not be a truly ancient garden – but surely the sombre twisted pine tree at the gate had taken centuries to attain its form and dignity. Pine and bamboo – trees that bend to the wind. Ludi had said that.

Mary felt that she was being initiated into a secret society that she had dreamt of – not knowing, that in truth, it existed. The snow now fell faster, thicker; a capricious puff of wind caused it to slant for a second. The wind caressed a bell hanging from a branch in a pine tree, and set the bell to ringing. *T-ring, t-ring!*

The winter breeze travelled on, and the bell, helpless without its assistance, was silent.

Instead of going on to the house, she turned and opened the heavy wooden gate that led to the street. Closing it behind her, she walked back to the hostel. Then, collecting her luggage, she drove through the streets of the city and out through the devastated suburbs, to the airport.

The atmosphere in the heated, crowded waiting-room was stifling. She sat there fighting her desire to run from this room and building, where people who had recently been enemies, now worked, talked, laughed, gave and received orders in the friendliest of manner. How senseless and ugly the war had been! As senseless and ugly, on a much larger scale, as her own past life.

The people in this room appeared to have forgotten the past. Their faces were bright, steps and actions alert with purpose, yet some of them, many of them, she suddenly realised, could have lived through more stringent and sorrowful experiences than hers.

Was there an ingredient lacking in her, the ingredient that gave humans the urge to make the best of their circumstances? The thought was frightening, gave her a future with no hope.

Why couldn't she have realised that life had presented her with a chance to garner strength from another human? One she could lean on, whose strengths and brashness would have complemented her, made her whole. Well! She hadn't realised – and that was that.

Removing her gloves, she looked at her hands. The scars there would never completely fade, but the pain that had caused the scars was now impossible to remember. Perhaps the pain and unhappiness that she was now feeling would, in time, also become only a memory.

The room bustled with animated movement, and, glancing at the clock, she saw that it was almost time to leave. The loudspeaker shouted instructions, and the harsh echo of the magnified voice hit back from the walls, bit into her nerves, so that she covered her eyes.

In the small, personal, dark cavern, her past life kaleidoscoped before her with a dizzying speed, and there was so little in it that was good to remember. Even her running away a few hours ago now appeared the most futile action in her life.

Why had she crept stealthily from that garden? Given up the chance of a future with the one person she loved?

Suzuki San had said, 'Sure he wants to see you,' and, in that garden, the realisation had come to her that he wished merely to see her because, for all his ruthlessness, he would not care to have her leave Japan with hurt feelings. He would have been sorry about walking out on her, would want to erase from his own memory the bitterness of their last meeting.

How strange it was, that a man and woman could have been together the way she and Ludi had once been; experience the close hot delight of passion as they had experienced it, and yet, hit out, take almost a sadistic joy in hurting one another.

Suddenly she knew, with clarity, that she and Ludi, with their so different backgrounds and characters, would always be bound to quarrel, irritate each other.

Like warring nations, throughout history, they could have warred, and made armistices, sometimes one the victor, sometimes the other. Someone was always the vanquished and, in the end, it didn't seem to make much difference.

How impercipient she had been! Not only had been, but was! Sitting here, ready to fly away, out of Ludi's life, without having taken the wild gamble that maybe, and, just perhaps, he had wanted to see her again because he loved her.

Was she courageous enough to take that gamble now? Without Ludi, there could be no happiness for her, no real life. Could she go to him now?

Uncovering her eyes, she rose to her feet. Her mind swirled with indecisions, then she knew with certainty that she should not go to his home, for she knew that if *Ludi* wanted anything, he went after it. If he wanted her, he would have managed to let her know.

Time to stop dreaming, Mary Sama, Suzuki San had once solemnly intoned.

For an instant, Mary again closed her eyes, and, in that instant, renounced dreams and hope. Then, longing for fresh air, she made her way across the lengthy busy foyer.

Halfway to the exit she stopped abruptly, for the thick glass door swung open, letting in a blast of cold, and Ludi Hoffer walked into the room.